The Bend in the Road: Refugees Writing

The Bend in the Road: Refugees Writing

Edited by Jennifer Langer

Five Leaves Publications

The Bend in the Road: Refugees Writing

Published in 1997 by Five Leaves Publications,
PO Box 81, Nottingham NG5 4ER.

Five Leaves Publications acknowledges
financial assistance from:

EAST
MIDLANDS
ARTS

Cover painting by Ron Waddams.

Design by 4 Sheets Design & Print.

Printed in the UK by Antony Rowe.

ISBN 0 907123 37 6

CONTENTS

I

II

Experiences of War in the Home Country

Further Reading

The Countries

The Contributors

INTRODUCTION

This is a book of very recent refugee literature by writers in exile originating from Bosnia, Iran, Iraq, Kurdistan, Somalia, Angola and Zaire.

Refugees bring with them a new culture, language and perspective and the writer in exile can be a link between cultures, nations and peoples. Through the literature, the reader gains an insight into the culture, life, experiences and thoughts of the writer.

The media frequently portray refugees as a stereotypical group who are disempowered, uneducated, illiterate victims intent on exploiting the host society's welfare and other systems. This book provides the opportunity to gain an insight not only into the pain of the refugee experience, manifested in alienation, marginalisation and loss of identity but also into the complexity and diversity of the experiences, concerns and issues of writers from different regions. The book is divided into themes which enable the reader to compare experience and genre. The themes are living in exile, prison and torture, fleeing, memories, women's experiences, suffering in the home country and resistance. Although there are many similarities of experience, the political situation in each country of origin is unique and range from the continued struggle for political rights in Kurdistan, factional warfare in Somalia, the complete suppression of opposition in Iraq and ethnic war in Bosnia.

All the literature in this book is by writers who fled from their countries because of persecution, war, imprisonment, lack of freedom of speech or censorship. The writer's role has often been quite different to his/her role in Britain. The writer's function may have been to mobilise ideological opposition and to express the anger of the people in stories and poems. In some of the countries covered, such as Somalia and Iraq, the writer is a

1

revered, well-known person in the community and the power of the pen is respected and often the only means of opposition and therefore, extremely dangerous for the writer. Salman Rushdie recently said that the duty of the writer is to say the unsayable, speak the unspeakable and to ask difficult questions. Because of his novel, the fatwa is still in force. Ken Saro-Wiwa, the playwright and revolutionary was executed in Nigeria in 1995. Taslima Nasreen, the Bangladeshi writer in exile, stated at a World University Service conference in 1995 that "It is the writer's responsibility to tell the truth." Esmail Kho'i, the Iranian poet in exile, tells a sick joke about an Iranian returning to Teheran after a long absence. "...He sets out to buy some cigarettes. 'But sir,' says the tobacconist, 'We don't sell cigarettes any more. I'm afraid you have to go to the butcher round the corner.' 'But butchers sell meat, don't they?' 'No sir, not any more. If you want to go to buy meat, you must go to the mosque, not far from here.' 'My God! But a mosque is a place where people go to say their prayers.' 'No sir, not any more. If you want to say your prayers, sir, you must go to the University of Tehran.' 'Good heavens! But that's a place for students and professors.' 'No, sir, not any more. If you want to meet the students and professors, you must go to Evin Prison.' 'But, for God's sake, isn't that a place for thieves and murderers?' 'No, sir, not yet. If you want to see the thieves and murderers, you must go to the Islamic Parliament.'"

Censorship is one of the serious threats to the freedom of the writer. In many cases, in order for a writer to remain in his or her country, there is a compulsion to operate a system of self-censorship or to veil one's ideas in allegory and imagery. Esmail Kho'i remarked in 1995 that "When I speak of censorship, I am speaking of about what is happening to the whole of Iranian poetry, to the whole of Iranian literature, to the whole of Iranian art, culture and life. Yes, life itself, has become the object of censorship in Iran."

The experience of exile, according to many of the writers, is a powerful stimulus to creativity because of the feelings and thoughts experienced. Clearly, the writer's role changes in an alien society and may alter perspective. Miroslav Jancic, at a poetry reading in 1996, stated that there were two definitions of homeland: "Language is my homeland" and "My country is where I feel." Esmail Kho'i has stated that a refugee is a split person - a typical example of a person in between, physically here but mentally there, unwilling to be in the host society but unable to go back.

Writers in exile face specific problems which are articulated in extracts from two articles: The Literature of Exile on Both Sides of the Chasm by A. Ebrahimi, Chair of Iranian PEN in Exile, and Refugee Blues by Predrag Finci, formerly Professor of Philosophy at Sarajevo University.

> Exile is one of the earliest phenomena in the history of humans' social condition. The political circumstances of the emigration, the demographic and economic fate of the disinherited group, the enforced experience in foreign lands, the language barrier and the rift between the exiled and the host community, are all key issues.
>
> Separation is a set of feelings and attitudes that isolates the expelled group from the majority. Once we acknowledge that exile is a mental condition and not a geographical one, that it removes people from their family, long-term friends, colleagues and their fellow-countrypersons and way of life, then the nature of this separation remains to be defined not only as a unilateral severance, but as something more profound.
>
> A refugee is not welcome anywhere. A person without a homeland is redundant everywhere.

A newcomer is not exactly denied his rights, but is never an equal, for he can never be 'the equal' with his hosts. He is an alien, a potential cause of mayhem and disorder and an extra burden in times of economic crisis. And there is no return. Or at least not for the time being.

'Once we had a country and we thought it fair
Look in the atlas and you'll find it there
We cannot go there now, my dear, we cannot go there now.'

The first great shock is language. The language keeps reminding us that we are in a completely foreign country. Wittgenstein's word that the boundaries of our language are the boundaries of our world acquires a clear existential meaning. As much as the lack of knowledge of the language torments the poorly educated, it troubles so much more those for whom a language is a medium of self-expression. What can a writer do whose mothertongue is not English? 'Poetry is what is lost in translation,' claimed Verlaine. A translated text is never my text. A language is my homeland, says a writer. From now on, his language will be the one he lives in, and the other one, revived in his dreams. A new language — a completely new culture. Many of them remain forever rooted in a world that no longer exists, spiritually absent in a world where they found themselves. Their past is destroyed, the present wretched, and the future?

A refugee is a person with no direction, disorientated in every way possible. It is all the same if he says the homeland is where the heart is or where he feels safe. It is of little consequence whether he was driven away from home or just fled. In the hell of militant nationalism, one could stay no longer; it is not a matter of whether one is a Serb, a Muslim, or a Croat any more... the question is whether one can be at all.

It is worth considering to what extent writing in liberty causes the writer to adapt, either in terms of theme, style or language. In his or her country feelings were expressed about conflict, conflict between individuals and authority, tradition and modernity, men and women. Widespread corruption or oppression and torture may have been exposed. In the West to which most writers have fled, these conflicts are more low key or nonexistent. The writer may lose his or her position of importance through working out of context. The reading or listening public may diminish substantially. Without exception the writers I contacted, for this anthology, were very keen for their work to be read by a wider public in order that their struggles could be understood.

Language is a key issue. The writer is usually unable to write effectively in the language of the new country and feels the loss of a language in which to communicate. Language is also very closely linked with identity. Predrag Finci expressed that above in his Refugee Blues. Jutkat T. Emoke says "Language is the basic tool of a writer. I seemed to lose my soul, my whole being. When my soul was burning to write a poem, a story, a book, I realised that I could hardly read the instructions for making a telephone call."

Language is closely related to power. The African writers here, from Angola, Zaire and Somalia, use a variety of languages. Many writers use the old colonial languages such as Portuguese or French, although some write in local languages. Although Somali only became a written language in 1972 it is used by Somali writers rather than English or Italian. Many stories are passed down from generation to generation in local languages. There are complex issues around publishing in Africa in terms of language choice, and often the reading public are wealthy and members of the leisured classes. In order to be published overseas, a colonial language needs to be used to reach a wider market. There is therefore a tension between the local oral tradition and wider publishing requirements.

Generally, in the societies described here, there is a greater dependence on the family and family structures and traditions, but the brutality and coarseness necessary for survival emanate from the short stories of Iraq and Iran for example. Women often have very clear roles and may be ostracised if they deviate from them. A female Zairean writer has written about the cruel injustice of male authority and male centred cultural practices.

My original intention was to focus on writers resident in Britain. However, it subsequently became clear that this should not be a criteria as writers in exile settle in the country most accessible to them in terms of immigration policies, historical links and presence of an existing community. The majority of writers included are resident in Britain but some live in Germany, Belgium, France, Holland, Switzerland and Canada.

The Literature

The literature was selected on the basis of some of the main countries from which refugees in the UK originate i.e. Angola, Zaire, Somalia, Iran, Iraq, Kurdistan and Bosnia. However the new trouble spots in the world, such as Rwanda and Algeria, have caused new groups of refugees to settle in Britain.

I used a range of sources. I made contact with a large number of writers in exile in the UK who kindly gave me their published or unpublished work for inclusion. A small amount of material had been published in English and some had appeared in the original country or in Britain in the original language. Some material was obtained from journals published here whilst other sources were specialist books published here or overseas. The Zairean contributions were generally provided by writers resident in other parts of Europe and sent to me.

Language and Translations

Clearly most writers write in their mothertongue and when he/she transfers to another country and culture, their literature may be out of context and, in any case, the author generally loses his/her audience. With regard to African literature, most writers from Angola and Zaire write in the colonial language i.e. Portuguese and French, although some local languages are used such as Umbundo, Lingala and Ciluba.

The issue of translations is an important one. Translating material is complex with cultural allusions being difficult to transfer and, in addition, translations may not be literal because of the difficulty of accessing language which is the precise equivalent.

Background Information

This is provided for each of the countries so that the literature can be set in a context. Given that writers have left their countries for political reasons, it was felt important to explain these. The literary/cultural background also helps the reader to gain a greater in-depth insight.

Acknowledgements

My sincere thanks to Hilary Paddon, Editor of *International Women's News* for her help and support.

My grateful thanks to Peter Beal for coming to my rescue electronically.

I am most grateful to all the following persons and writers, some of whom I met clandestinely in obscure cafes and venues around the capital and some of whom gave me hospitality in their homes: *Haifa Zangana, Fatima Al-Mohsen* — Editor of *Nsus, Fawzi Kerim, Zuhair al-Jazairi, Lily al-Tair* — Translator of Arabic, *Xenia Wilding* — Co-ordinator, Bosnian Refugee Information Centre, *Kamal Miroudy* — Co-ordinator, Kurdish Information Centre, *Ahmad Ebrahimi* — Chair, Iranian PEN in Exile, *Igor Klikovac* — Editor of *Stone Soup, Abdul Karim Kassid* — Editor of *Nsus, Hal Abuur, Vanessa Vasic* — Journalist on *War Report, Sadia Ahmed* — Editor of *Hal Abuur, Sheri Lazar* — Co-ordinator, Kurdish Workers' Association, *Denise Ganderton* — Secretary, Association for the Study of Caribbean and African Literature in French, *Francois Itangu Ngondo & Jean-Marie Witele* — Co-ordinators, Islington Zairean Refugee Group, *Antonio Cabral, Martin Orwin* — School of Oriental and African Studies, London University, *Professor Z. Lesic* — School of Slavonic Studies, London University, *Sava Peic* — The British Library, Slavonic and East European Collections and *Barbara Blend* — Teacher of French.

I would also like to thank: *Jane Spender* — International PEN, *Philip Spender* — *Index on Censorship,* Iraqi Community Association, Hammersmith, Francophone Africa Research Centre, University of Westminster, and the Library for Iranian Studies, Acton.

Jennifer Langer

IN EXILE

Forces Invisibles
by Mabiala Molu (Zaire)

Dieu
    du
        Ciel

Sorciers
    Terrestres

Magiciens
    de
        L'enfer

Forces
    Invisibles

Profondeurs
    Insondables

Qui
    Me
        Délivrera
            De ces

Tourments insolubles.

Invisible Forces
by Mabiala Molu (Zaire)

God
 of the
  Sky

Terrestrial
  Sorcerers

Magicians
 of
  Hell

Invisible
 Forces

Unfathomable
 Depths

Who
 Will
  Deliver
  Me
  From these

Unceasing Torments

(Translated by Jennifer Langer)

A Letter

by Himzo Skorupan (Bosnia)

My dear sister,

I am writing to you from afar. I have found myself in this godforsaken place where the snow would not melt. My granddaughter told me the other day that the North Pole (whatever that is) is not far from us, but heck if I am gonna check that one out.

Word has it we are in Norway, some say we are in Sweden, so I truly do not know who to believe. Wish you were here to sip coffee with someone dear and near. To tell you the truth, I have never heard of your whatchamacallit Malasia. Do tell me if it snows there, I will send you some wool socks and a warm jumper. How are you doing? I — poorly. At least days go by, somehow, but nights drag on forever. I don't know what is worse: when I stay awake all night long, or when I fall asleep and dream. During the day I make myself busy, and old as I am, I have to learn this darned language. All three constituent nations from Bosnia attend out language course, and there is also a Jewish woman from Sarajevo, so it is widely thought that we could communicate better with each other after we have learned their language! The fact is, once we all return to Bosnia, we'll have to talk through a translator, or by sign language. We'll look pretty much like the UN Assembly on the East River. Mind you, this language of theirs won't go through my thick head, but I am relieved when I think of the wretched souls who ended in Japan. I reckon Japanese is mighty hard to learn.

Apart from the language course, I have found yet another pastime — philately, that is, stamp collecting. I correspond with our folks from six different countries, and every time a letter arrives, I take off the stamps first. I bought an album and a magnifying glass. If you want me to, I can send you the spare ones. Do tell me, if you're interested.

Neither Here Nor There
by Himzo Skorupan (Bosnia)
from Diary of an Exile, London Notes

I had my trepidations for a long time.
But yesterday, I could wait no more.
I went to the phone and dialled a number: my number!
At the other end of the line, in my house, I heard an unknown voice saying that I wasn't there. I asked him if he knew what had happened to me, where I was, and he said that he had moved in recently and that he didn't know.
I know perfectly well where I am, but I wondered whose head was on my pillow, who was browsing through my books, who was looking at the pictures on my walls....I wanted to know who was picking fruit in my garden and what had happened to my plants.
And I started thinking.
What does he dream about while resting on my pillow?
Is he afraid he might choke when biting into apples picked in my garden?
Is he enjoying the scent of my plants?
Does he feel uncomfortable in my bed?
What does he say when he hears someone knocking at the door?
What does he see in the pictures on my walls?
My books, he doesn't read, I know that!
God have mercy on him!
And this is the way things are: I am not really here, and over there, I am no more.

Waterloo
by Miroslav Jancic (Bosnia)

Stop glancing at that man over there
Who is leaning on that anti-racist poster
He is squinting through you
As if you were smuggling
A can of gas from the Tokyo Underground
A bomb like those from the Paris Metro
Or fertiliser explosive from Oklahoma.

You are to blame
It's the damned telepathy
Why the hell you had to recapitulate just now
That your Star Trek bag contains
A can of bitter
A shrapnel which missed you by an inch in Sarajevo —
You are a missed person, you must admit —
And the stuff eerie indeed
A handful of the soil still smelling with gunpowder

What's more
There is that idyllic family album
Those clandestine manuscripts of yours
All that might additionally compromise
The fragile identity of a not repatriable refugee
From the South — and your toothbrush without tooth-
paste
And the stop is Waterloo.

Omnia mea secum porto,
You would try to confuse the detective by Latin;
Pity is the last thing you enjoy, yes
And let them accuse you of lacking despair;
As soon as the Northern Line arrives
You shall jump in and reconsider your behaviour.

13

The Mailed Parcel
by Ibrahim Ahmed (Iraq)

On that day they did not have any lessons at the language school. They were busy with the domestic chores when the mail-flap clicked. He remarked to his wife that this time they may have dropped through some coupons for flour, and quickly went to find out.

On top of the usual colourful papers he found a dark-coloured parcel. He examined it calmly. He thought it had been delivered to him by mistake, but discovered that it was addressed to him in vague handwriting as if the sender was not fully certain of his address. But where had the sender obtained his address from? He remembered, in the camps, he had exchanged addresses with Iraqi refugees, to keep in touch in the course of their long path ahead.

He was about to open it eagerly, but his fingers stopped at the edges of the parcel; he was suddenly overwhelmed with fear. It occurred to him it might be a parcel bomb. He remembered what he had seen on television a few days ago about an explosion in which a Kurdish woman and her daughter had both been killed by a parcel bomb. What exacerbated his unease, was that the parcel was from abroad with Czech stamps on it and no name of the sender only postmarks and some deletions and scribbles added. So this parcel was on his trail throughout his wanderings among the camps. It might have been sent to him to his first address in Sweden. He thought it unlikely for a parcel bomb to pass through all those places undetected. His wife came to him, prompting him and inquiring: "What is this?" but he quickly signalled to her cautiously when she was about to pick it up. He distanced her from it saying: "It might be booby-trapped". She carried on looking at him disconcertedly and said: "Who are we, for them to send us a parcel bomb?"

He had stopped his political work after they had had a child. When he worked in politics, he had been neither a

14

leader nor a prominent figure. He said: "And what was the Kurdish woman and her daughter up to when they murdered them with a parcel bomb?" The wife said: "We have been forsaken to the end of the world." He said, while staring at the parcel: "Sometimes they murder people of lesser significance than ourselves to frighten others!"

He carefully placed the parcel in an empty corner by the door.

For a long time now, they had stopped expecting mail. In Algeria, almost a year after leaving Iraq, their first and only son had drowned at the seaside when they were on an outing. The shock had almost crushed them both. They were frightened of informing their families in Iraq who were attached to the child for when they were leaving, they had asked to keep the child. A cryptic letter had arrived from their families requesting that they did not correspond with them; but they understood. Their families, like others, received their mail from the party headquarters and security bureaus of their districts. Yet they still feared receiving a letter from the family asking about the child.

Their letter to friends abroad were spasmodic and reluctant and had now stopped for they carried no news other than catastrophes, tragedies and misfortunes which they could no longer bear to hear about. They now feared the postman and were scared when he appeared, repeating to each other that they "could no longer handle a letter".

They had had two children in the course of their migration to various countries. They had arrived in Sweden not more than a year ago, anguished by exile. Their savings had dwindled. They had been transported to various refugee camps and were sent to live in a small town by the sea.

In the first week of their arrival, they received a letter with a plastic green key from one of the supermarkets inviting them to collect 250 grams of coffee, as a token of hospitality and welcome. It was a successful commercial and humane gesture.

The man held the letter fearlessly, remarking to his wife that no longer was coffee the Arab symbol of hospitality and magnanimity. In the many Arab countries in which they had found themselves, they had been received with annoyance, dejection and meanness. In Algeria, when their child had drowned, the father's spirit and health had been destroyed, and yet they did not renew his teaching contract but asked him instead to vacate the house and country within weeks.

Here they had found security, peace and a carefree life marred only when they saw in each other's eyes, the waves of the sea in the darkness of the nights carrying them to the vortex of that distant past and its devastating nightmares awakening in their hearts the vision of that beautiful child drowning and fading in front on their eyes in the nearby deeps of the sea, while they both stood helplessly looking on.

They busied themselves learning the Swedish language in preparation for work.

Everyday when the man heard the click of the mail-flap, his heart would throb; getting to the front door was like reaching a haunted place at night. But as he often found magazines, supermarket adverts and colourful fliers with attractive offers for foods, clothes, cars and castles, mingled every so often with one or two letters from friends or the local authorities, he shook his head and laughed, remarking to his wife "Perhaps all the junk mail has had one benefit. It has enabled us to hold a letter again."

Up to now, they had found opening letters in this part of the world an experience that was not frightening. It no longer seemed to them, as it once had, like the opening of a grave. They now felt able to receive letters from their families and to reply to their questions. They did not, however, dwell too much on such hopes since their families had heard nothing from them for some years now. They too did not know what had become of them, or whether their address had changed since the Authorities and the Party still regulated everything.

The man was happy to hear the clicking sound of the metal mail-flap. It sounded like the rustling of two heavy twigs dropping their ripe fruits on the ground. The pictures of commodities and the advertisements with their bright colours and prices, consoled him as it made him feel that there existed a world immersed in benevolence and pleasure, not catastrophe.

But this parcel in the corner seems to him now something else. He approached it imagining that it might explode in the faces of his two children on their return from school. His wife told him to place it on the balcony, but changed her mind when she remembered that it was covered in snow. The man became irritated and said: "Shall we call the police?" The wife was in a calmer state and replied: "We will show it to the postman."

But the man thought it horrifying to spend the night with a bomb in the house. The wife sensed this through his anxious glances and unrest and said she wanted to go shopping and that he could accompany her to the post office which was on the way. He decided to risk carrying the parcel. As he walked on the snow, the chill winds penetrating, he feared he might slip and that the parcel would land on him. So he walked slowly, careful not to shape the parcel or collide with one of the pedestrians on the snowy, narrow pavements. He kept a reasonable distance from his wife thinking that at least she should survive for the sake of the two children. With the hand carrying the parcel stretched away from his body, he persuaded himself that the explosion might sever his hand, which would be a reasonable sacrifice, but would not affect the rest of his body.

At the post office, in a mixture of English and Swedish, they spoke to a beautiful girl who sought the advice of one of the officers inside who carefully checked the parcel and said confidently: "It is perfectly normal and safe." When he saw they were both still apprehensive and looking at him in despair and sadness, he said to them: "Do you wish me to open it?" The man nodded his head hastily. The officer opened the parcel and passed it to the man. The man removed the contents of the parcel and found a letter:

"I could find no resting place. I have moved about a great deal. I am now clearing everything to prepare to emigrate to Australia. I did not wish to lose your precious belongings. I am certain that both of you with your two beautiful children look upon the past with strength and courage." He opened another old and faded envelope. He found between his now trembling hands, a picture of their drowned child and a lock of his hair. The Swedish officer could not understand why this man uttered a loud moan and why the woman broke down in tears. He began to look at them and at this place in which calm and order reigned. It seemed to him as if something had exploded which he had not heard!

(Translated by Lily Al-Tai)

The Poor Fellow in Paris
by Mabiala Molu (Zaire)

Like a dream
A poor fellow in Paris
Walking alone among
The deepest wilderness of Paris
The most closed and self-centred city
Dream becomes nightmare
No greeting, no smile, nothingness
The poor fellow in Paris
Thinking of the inner darkness of his village
When teeth sing of happiness
Where all people are brothers
The poor fellow in Paris
Into the solitude of the distressed crowd
Having the blues
Afraid of his dark shadow
Lonely into a homelessness
Boosted to hear God's voice
The poor fellow in Paris
Sick by winter time
Disappointed by a dull and scared sun
Flung by taciturn people
Not happy, no way
The poor fellow in Paris

Les Etoiles Ecrasées (The Shattered Stars)
by Pius Ngandu Nkashama (Zaire)
(Extract from the novel)

Joachim Mboyo, a Zairean widely respected for his football prowess, was living quietly in Brussels, Belgium.

Gerbek's image came back to him like a slap in the face. He gulped in a mouthful of cold air. Joachim noisily breathed out thick vapour which dispersed in the mist. He brushed it away out of sight. A mute anger suffocated him. Pieces of wall seemed to waver. The whole of the Grande-Place spun round dizzily with its belfries and spires pointing up into the emptiness of the grey sky. The cruciform towers shook as if about to collapse. He was powerless to keep them upright. A cataclysm, an earthquake, was what he wished for. When the apocalypse came, the entire city would be plunged into the white-hot lava of fire surging out of the bowels of the earth. These old buildings would collapse in a deafening explosion to restore some calm to him.

The sound of swearing hit him head on.

"Dirty Congolese, can't you look where you're going, bloody idiot!" He had collided with a drunkard who swayed, dragging along his rages and wine bottles in a wave of suffocating smells. With his free hand, the tramp whirled around, making an obscene gesture as if he intended to strangle someone.

Joachim Mboyo felt like throwing himself on this stinking body of rages devoured by lice and attacked by grubs. It was easy to resent this fellow with his shaggy, unkempt hair, rejected by his own society and whose only prospect was the lime of the pauper's grave. He heard himself mutter in spite of himself.

"Sorry sir. I didn't do it on purpose. Please excuse me."

"Son of a bitch. Move yourself and stop bugging everyone with your 'Sorry sir,' you idiot!" The tramp's scathing reply resounded dryly. Joachim continued to stammer, a bitter taste in his mouth. "I said 'Excuse me sir' and that will have to do."

"If you don't know how in behave in civilised society, Nigger, go back to the equatorial jungle. There are still orang-utans on the trees there and those monkeys think that anything goes."

Joachim Mboyo brought up both hands. He so much wanted to hit this little man who couldn't even keep his balance. He felt himself covering his ears to block off the sound. He would explode if had to go on suffering from those yelling voices. He began to run to escape from his own nightmare. The drunkard's shouting followed him and was lost in the mist. He had disappeared from view now. The echoes dissipated behind the colonnades and the overwhelming stench of the rags died away.

(Translated by Jennifer Langer)

Return to Neverland-upon-Rupture
by Ahmad Ebrahimi (Iran)
English version dedicated to
Esmail Kho'i and Karina Zabihi

What would be the point of departure
to return to Neverland-upon-Rupture
at this or any other juncture?
After cycling on for years in different circles
breaking up and going round in a loop,
turning all the time, pedalling away exhaustion
turning away, from friend and foes,
yet giving way to the nostalgic impulse
in our toes.

What would be the point of departure
even now that we have to stop altogether?
watching each other's hearts retire,
searching but not finding the magic glue
to repair this odd yet very old puncture
with blow job
hardly meant for the tyre
to arrive, finally, in the future.

Spared from the firing squad and torture
but not from the fire of one burning wish,
yet knowing deep down that it will never come true for us.
a new wheel, a ready tyre and a gun to fire.

Dorothy didn't know that her shoes
could have always returned her to Kansas
we somehow knew, but discarded ours long ago,
to walk away from life barefoot
on the fire of only one exclusive desire.
Eventually we are bound to understand the impasse,
our limited resources and the power of black satire.
Even if the world is not burning with

our exclusive desire,
we must be thank thankful for our stay —
a stay of execution you may say.
But in this mix of lifeless love and crossfire —
OK — call it the purgatory of leave to stay in the UK,
we have to find a way before we retire
to be able to entertain all kinds of interests, desire:
retaining the Ashes, Dad's Army and
"England, your England" as George Orwell wrote after
reluctantly shooting the Elephant — maybe as a farewell
to the British Empire.
Then the world around us would have a chance
to understand our unnurtured nature
and we take it to be our true home
— whether London, Karachi, Ankara or Rome.

Neverland-upon-Rupture
from a distance, one can see the landscape
inviting as an intoxicating mirage, a dead sea of flesh.
but when one closely inspects the texture
it turns out to be a mirage of shimmering wine
which nevertheless makes you tipsy
as long as you are asleep and dreaming.
But the moment you wake up, there is little mercy.
You have to run from one corner to another
tracing the footprints of "the testifying Goddess of Youth"
in vain, only to see in yourself
Hagar, abandoned by the Prophet Abraham
running the seven hills of despair and thirst
carrying the almost dead baby of hope
in search of the bosom of water,
but to no avail.

And the Motherland
an empty dessert-bowl of breast
that does not answer
the desperate call of your pitiful heart.
And roots
that strangle you without haste.

What would be the point of return?
A return
to Neverland-upon-Rupture
even for the sake of dying there
too late to contemplate victory,
too exhausted to surrender.

The blue sky is no longer in the air
when you set foot on that particular part of the sphere.
We are trapped in past continuous.
For us there is no longer a future to share.
Why then, tell me
you still care
to return there
to Neverland-upon-Rupture
at this or any other juncture?

*(Translated from Persian for the English PEN Poetry
Evening 3 May 1995)*

Lone, Lorn London
by Sousa Jamba (Angola)

Sousa Jamba finds that it is not easy for an African to meet a girlfriend.

When I was told in Africa that people in a Western metropolis could be lonely, I did not believe it. I imagined London, for instance, with ten million people, which was double the total population of Zambia, where I grew up. I imagined that if anyone felt lonely he would simply walk out and talk to people. After three years in London, I have come to discover that it is not that simple.

One of the first things I wanted after a week in London was a girlfriend: someone I would write poems for, take to films and symphony orchestras. I had once read a short story by an African writer in which he described a romantic walk with a charming white girl on Hampstead Heath. I too hoped to take my girlfriend there.

I went to the local McDonalds in search of a girlfriend. I ordered myself a King Burger and a family size orange juice and settled beside two girls. As I ate the burger and sipped the orange juice, my eyes switched from the *Sun* to the two girls. I noticed a funny story in the *Sun* and showed it to the two girls. I thought this was a way of breaking down the barriers between us, in order to start conversing. The girls giggled over the story and left, not wanting to say a word to me.

I had to think of a strategy. In Zambia, my contemporaries and I had adopted what we then considered an impressive way of starting a conversation with girls in the street. On approaching an interesting girl the proper thing to say was: "Hello Baby, did I see you somewhere in Washington or was it in Tokyo? Paris perhaps?" The girl would then allow herself a little titter and say she had never been out of Zambia. Of course she knew that the boy had never been out of Zambia, either. But that was part of the game.

The next thing to was to say how beautiful she was. The line for this was: "If roses were black they would be like you."

I tried this strategy in London; just the first lines, that is. It failed. The girls would simply answer no and give me an angry look. I befriended a Nigerian student who claimed to know the way out of my dilemma. He said he knew the way to ingratiate oneself with British girls. His line was: "Hello, I come from Nigeria."

Whenever my Nigerian friend repeated how sound his advice was, it was as though I became seized by fits of jingoism. I told him that nothing short of death would make me say that I was not an Angolan. He would look at me, shake his head, and say: "It is your problem, my friend. These people here are very stupid. They've never heard of Angola, so they will think you come from one of those countries where people walk naked. But Nigeria, they all know it. I mean these people fear Nigeria. Tell girl that you are from Nigeria; the first thought that comes to her mind is money. I mean we have money."

I told this to a British girl who just wanted to be a friend of mine. She said my Nigerian friend was a Male Chauvinist Pig. British girls, she said, went for lover. I asked her how I would come into contact with them. She said night-clubs. But before going to these night-clubs, she said, I was to divest myself of some attitudes which, she suspected, were common to most African men. British girls, she said, hated sexism and men who were too proud to show their emotions.

I went to a night-club ready to dance attendance upon my would-be girlfriends and to break into tears once overwhelmed by love. The Empire in Leicester Square was filled on this night with Japanese tourists who danced with their cameras strapped to their necks. At the entrance, a few steps from the cloakroom, couples were kissing passionately. I saw a few black boys — I took them for African — kissing British girls. Soon, I hoped, I was going to join them.

In Africa, people never kiss in public. A woman who allows herself to be kissed in public is said to have loose morals. Everything (moral or immoral) is supposed to be done indoors. But we considered ourselves civilised. At the school I went to, for instance, we used to kiss girls at the back of the hall when films were being shown: and at night after prep, we escorted them to their dormitories and kissed them goodnight, in full view of the junior boys, who, it was said, were "cryptic voyeurs". So if I found myself a girlfriend, there was nothing wrong in kissing her in Oxford Street, for it was admissible in the Western culture of which I considered myself a part.

I asked several girls to dance with me: they refused and walked away. I went back to my British friend and told her that I had tried my best at the Empire to no avail. What was I going to do next?

She said the Empire was not the right place for someone like me (I had presented myself as a poet); that it was full of tourists. She gave me a list of proper clubs. But there was another drawback — my clothes. It is very easy to tell an African man by the clothes he wears: they tend to be bright-coloured and oftentimes baggy. My British friend told me that London girls prefer duller colours. If, however, I was to present myself as a student, then a ragged pair of faded jeans were preferable. My friend is what I later came to be told counted as trendy. I declined her advice and stuck to my checked trousers, bright shirts and bright shoes.

I never gave up the search. One day I saw a beautiful girl who enthralled me. I went to her and said "Hello, have I seen you in Washington before?" She looked startled. "I was actually born there. Where in Washington did you see me?" I began to scratch my head and confessed that I had never been there. That night, I went home and wrote a poem in which I compared her beauty to that of the mighty Victoria Falls. She was to become my girlfriend for over a year. And then we split. I was once again back to square one.

Whitewashed Houses
by Abdirahman Mirreh (Somalia)

What a pleasure to be
in such a whitewashed city
watching the fishermen
mending the nets.

Standing at the quay from
where the Vikings rowed
their boats through morning
mist.

What a beautiful rainy day
sitting in a bus after the
sunset, the mountains
on the left, the fjords on
the right.

Here comes the spring a
few days early to touch
the trees to awaken the
flower, seeds beneath
the earth.

Hiding Place
by Abdirahman Mirreh (Somalia)

Not my intention to meet him
a Moslem man who owned a shop
selling the Koran-Kitab.

Nor he thought he would meet
his like in such an isolated place.

He sipped his glass of beer
in a dark corner of the pub
and as our eyes met
he cast his to the floor.

I felt so sorry disturbing the enjoyment
in his hiding he sought
oh... If I only knew.

Hospital Sketches on Old Age
by Esmail Kho'i (Iran)

1. Dreams So Young

I am an old man with dreams so young
I run so fast, but inside my mind.
Compared with the weak, I am so strong.
And have such good eyes, compared with the blind.

I was going to meet my lovely woman
at six o'clock, somewhere this nearby.
It is eight already — damn you, old man!
Run! To be in time to see her goodbye.
                    3 April 93

2. To Do

Takes him half an hour
to put his coat on
by which time the desire
to go out
    is gone!
                    3 April 93

3. Little Snail

— Little snail! Where are you hurrying?

— I am late. Sir, please let me pass.
I have a date with my beloved.
seven blades down round the next grass.
                    3 April 93

4. A Dawn of Smiles

And a bird called "Hello"
— of all the words —
singing
on the wings of the morning breeze,
to start
the symphony of the early birds.

Ah,
you lucky fellow!
4 April 93

5. Proverbial

Early to bed, early to rise:
unhealthy, unwealthy, unwise.
4 April 93

6. Not Remembering

Father of three, grandfather to four.
To himself a pain, to the nurse a bore.
"I want to go home", he keeps moaning,
not remembering where home is any more.
4 April 93

7. The Nurse

"Michelle" is her name
a blooming butterfly,
wasted
on withered foliage.
4 April 93

31

8. Nurses

No descendants
of
Florence Nightingale
"In thought and word and deed":
her descendance,
    indeed.
into
the absent presence
of routined minds
behind cheerless faces
above hospital uniforms,
treating all cases
and forms
of human disease
with the same degree
of mindless ease.

"Please,
  Nurse!.."
you are to rehearse
as how to plead:
"Here, Nurse! Please.."
before you receive
the standard answer:
    "Sir!
There are others, too,
in urgent need
much more than you."

Yet, you cannot help pleading:
for it is not your heart,
but your throbbing wound
that is bleeding.
                4 April 93

9. The Job that is Nursing

No.
not a trace
of grace
in the things they say
or do.
among themselves
or to you.

But this is your second day;
and
by now
you know
they are just Nurses
their hearts in their purses,
filled with the coy
joy
of having a job:
Their ward of patients,
    an unruly mob,
to be tamed
into submitting
to the rules
of professional Disinterestedness
which demand
that you say
Nothing
as you pay
Nothing
for what you are always about to receive:
the Doctor's blessed permission
to heave your last relieving sigh
and die.
            7 April 93

10. What Happened?

— Where is this hell of misery and pain?

— North Middlesex Hospital,
or what is left of it.

— What happened to that paradise of medicine?

— the Tories.

The Barbarians came
back.
                    7 April 93

11. Prayer

"I'm dying, God! I'm dying"
The old wretch keeps crying.

Grant, god, for pity's sake,
that this once he is not lying.
                    4 April 93

12. Down Came the Curtain

What filled the ward with fear
was not that death was near:
It was the way the Nurse said:
"Sister! Sister! He is dead."
                    4 April 93

Fleeing

Fleeing
by Abdirahman Mirreh (Somalia)

And as we walked
we crossed
the Golis Ranges
Wadis and the
Ununuf plain.

Fearing the soldiers
who killed my sister
and thousand others
too.

We walked by
night stumbling
on volcanic rocks
sharper than
butchers' knives

The feet bleeding
we had to walk
I touched a
stone with my lips
as I fell
the moon didn't
shine it helped us.

Zlata's Diary
by Zlata Filipovic (Bosnia)

In her personal account of the war in Sarajevo, Zlata, a young schoolgirl, describes the nightmare her life became once the killing began. For over two years she was trapped in her own home with no water, gas or electricity.

Zlata recalls the last few days in Sarajevo and her arrival in Paris.

Dear Mimmy,

PARIS. There's electricity, there's water, there's gas. There's, there's... life, Mimmy. Yes, life; bright lights, traffic, people, food... Don't think I've gone nuts, Mimmy. Hey, listen to me, Paris!? No, I'm not crazy, I'm not kidding. It really is Paris and (can you believe it?) I'm here. Me, my mum and my dad. At last. You're 100 per cent sure I'm crazy, but I'm serious, I'm telling you; dear Mimmy, that I have arrived in Paris. The darkness is behind us, now we're bathed in light lit by good people. Remember that — good people. Bulb by bulb, not candles, but bulb by bulb, and me bathing in the lights of Paris. Yes, Paris. Incredible.

You don't understand. You know, I don't think I understand either. I feel as though I must be crazy, dreaming; as though it's a fairy tale, but it's all TRUE. All right, let me explain.

On 6 December, three days after my thirteenth birthday (my second in the war), the publishers told us that on Wednesday 8 December, we were to be ready, that they would be coming for us — we were going to Paris for your promotion, Mimmy. It was a real shock. Although that's what I had wanted, I had wanted to leave that hell, to escape with my parents from death, hunger, the cold, because it really had become unbearable, but it was a shock all the same. We had one day to accept that we were

36

leaving Sarajevo, to say our goodbyes to Grandma and Grandpa, the whole family, Mirna, to pack and be ready by 8.00 a.m. on Wednesday 8 December when an UNPROFOR personnel carrier would be coming to pick us up. For me, the hardest part was to accept that I was going, that I was leaving behind the people I loved, knowing the situation I was leaving them in. I was leaving them in war, in misery, without water, electricity, gas or food. And who knew when or if I would ever see them again.

It's impossible to explain those mixed feelings of sorrow and joy. Joy at being able to leave the war and sorrow at having to leave EVERYTHING behind. ALL MY LOVED ONES. Oh, Mimmy, all those tears. I cried and my loved ones cried. When I packed my things I cried and I think that all those things that were supposed to go with me, like those that remained behind maybe to wait for me one day in Sarajevo, cried too. I wanted to take everything, because I was equally fond of everything, but it wouldn't all fit into one suitcase. I had to choose. It was hard and it was sad.

The day was short and most of it was spent in tears, while the equally short night was spent packing, by candlelight, again in tears.

Wednesday 8 December, 8.00 a.m. It was all done. We had cried our eyes out, said our goodbyes, packed for the trip which was going to be who knows how long? Eight o'clock came and went. No personnel carrier. Why? Who knows? Something went wrong. Again that strange mixed feeling, again that feeling of sunken hopes.

At 10.00 a.m. on 23 December, the personnel carrier actually came. Through the little window of the vehicle I watched the Post Office pass by, the Law Faculty, the Holiday Inn, Marin Dvor, Pofalici, Hrasno, Alipasino polje, Nedazarici. Sarajevo was passing by. We reached the airport safely. Everybody there kindly welcomed us. Every so often our eyes welled up with tears because there was that strange ever-present mixed feeling of sorrow and joy.

Then the Hercules cargo plane, flying over Bosnia and Herzegovina, leaving it behind. We flew over the Adriatic Sea. I saw it all from the pilot's cabin. Our landing point — Ancona. And... we stepped out of the Hercules and together with Mr. Rufin, our friend Jean-Christophe Rufin, we boarded a small plane belonging to the French government and then — destination PARIS. In the plane we were given Coca Cola, salmon, eggs, steak, chicken, tomatoes... YUMMY. Everything I hadn't seen for almost two years.

And then... the lights of Paris appeared. There was electricity. Then I caught sight of the Eiffel Tower, Arc de Triomphe, cars, houses, roads, people...LIFE. At about 3.00 p.m. we landed at the military airport in Paris. A wonderful reception, warm words of welcome.

After the airport, we were driven to the Cercle Nationale des Armees hotel. Then a SHOWER. WATER. BATH. HOT WATER. COLD WATER. SHAMPOO. SHOWER. Bliss! We spent about an hour in the water and then we had to go to the television studios.

That's how Paris welcomed me. That's how I came out of the darkness and saw the lights. Are these lights my lights as well? I wonder. When even a glimmer of this light illuminates the darkness of Sarajevo, then it will be my light as well. Until then...???

Zlata

Getting Ready for a Trip
by Igor Klikovac (Bosnia)

Getting ready for a trip. In a borrowed sports bag
you pile clothes upon books. Paltry things which are out of
sight,
you deliberately forget. You sing to yourself.
Unbidden haste — a Czech tourist's itching feet — spurs
you on.

You'd like to go as far as possible, but zipping up the bag,
you feel you've already arrived somewhere.
Opened scissors on the table, small change in the lee-side
of a pocket.

Outside the mortars are thundering — the distance you
are now,
you'll never make it.

Too Many Shooting Stars
by Miroslav Jancic (Bosnia)

The mighty white ferryboat Slavia
Ploughs through the ever bluer Adriatic Sea
In the middle of a blessed late summer night:
The sky has displayed all its jewellery
Ulysses marvelled at the same.

Yet the usual romance is missing
An elderly singer is delivering messages
Over the loudspeaker:
Thrust love/Love is almighty, or so
Whilst the ship's engine is definitely throbbing
Love-is-gone/Love-is-gone-for-ever
As a refrain.

Whilst cruising into the unknown
I'm alone on the deck
Keeping my eye on a shooting star
Which is tearing the horizon over the mainland
By its long, long tail;
Before I succeeded in expressing any wish
Another appeared from the opposite direction.

The sky is shattered
All of a sudden there are so many shooting stars
That one simply doesn't know what to wish
As his homeland is vanishing for good
In a deep, deep night.

How We Fled from Angola
by Sousa Jamba (Angola)

In February 1976, the civil war came to Huambo. It was one of those lovely African afternoons when it is neither too cold nor too hot. Rumours were spreading that the Cubans were at Acmol, a suburb of Huambo. I came home from school and found my sister packing.

Everyone was on the move. I had never seen so many anxious people. The next day we reached Silva Porto, where my aunt Teodora had an orchard with gigantic pears. All the townspeople were preparing to leave.

Serpa Pinto had been one of the most beautiful towns in Angola. Astride the River Cubango, the Portuguese had built some magnificent hotels, but they were already bullet-riddled and so filthy that people preferred to sleep in the open. Most of the people who had come this far supported Unita and the young men were enthusiastic about going as guerrillas to the war.

It was decided that we drive to Cuito Cuanavale and walk from there to the Zambian border, 180 miles away. It was at Cuito that I first saw a Mig fighter. It glinted silver in the sky, flashed over us menacingly and emitted several terrifying thunderclaps.

We were now in the forest, guided by an old map of Angola some one had plucked from a classroom wall. This map was to prove disastrous. The older people, whose map-reading left much to be desired, argued continually as to whether the stream in front of us was the river on the map. It often turned out that the river in question was not a river at all but a huge swamp.

The squabbling continued and our group, which numbered a thousand, broke into factions. Our faction was led at first by Alfredo Sachipangele, a medical assistant who thought that he was a doctor and bored us all with the stories of the operations that he had performed. He had also read so much of the Bible that he thought that he was a

41

priest. He navigated by the position of the sun. I will never walk so far again.

Our reserves of food soon finished and we had to turn to nature. Fortunately, it was the rainy season and there were many caterpillars. There was one variety that was delicious when properly cooked but another furry kind which I detested, though it was reputed to have medicinal properties. As we moved deeper into the forest food became scarcer, and no living creature that could pass through fire was spared. Many of our group died after eating wild mushrooms. One man died after eating an onion-like plant which caused his stomach to swell. My brother-in-law used to tantalise us by describing kapenta, a kind of fish available in Zambia.

Alfredo walked the whole journey with a stethoscope round his neck, telling people to stick out their tongues, and looking beneath their eyelids to see whether they had enough blood, as he put it. Among those who died was Elder, a boy whom I had never liked because he was cleverer then I. He used to correct my Portuguese pronunciation. Unlike me, he had been brought up in comfortable circumstances in which milk was not a luxury, and therefore found the hardships of the forest more hard to bear. He scarcely ate anything, while we obeyed the Portuguese proverb: *come sujo guarda a vida* (eat dirt to save your life). He died of diarrhoea and vomiting. He was buried in a Unita flag (the only cloth available) in a shallow grave by the banks of the River Quembo.

During the funeral, I voraciously eyed the pot of caterpillars. Alfredo, of course, preached a sermon and the women begged the exhausted men to dig the grave deeper so that the hyenas would not dig up Elder's body and eat it.

Water was another hazard. We had to drink water contaminated by mud and animal droppings. The banks of one of the rivers that we crossed had reputedly been mined by the Portuguese during the war of liberation and we had to follow the animal tracks for the sake of safety. As we were walking across a swamp I saw a woman lose two young children who were sucked downwards into the swamp and whose only tombs were a few transient bubbles breaking the surface.

Crossing the River Quembo was a problem. The men, who now numbered 30, were too weak to swim. One man, however, made it across the river, but his skin was lacerated by sharp reeds. Covered in blood, some villagers on the other side thought he was a messenger from God, because they had never known anyone swim the river before. They sent canoes to fetch the rest of us.

After crossing the Quembo, food was easier to come by because there were more villages. In one of them I was treated for worms by the local herbsman in a way I found repulsive. Five strong men, however, ensured I took my medicine and I was too weak to resist.

At a village near the Zambian border we were surrounded by a gang of men with grenade-launchers and automatic rifles. Their leader wanted to take my sister as a wife. She wept, I wept and trembled. My brother-in-law argued that we were simple peasants without political opinions or significance; but later he told us that he was thinking of grabbing one of their rifles and killing them all. The gang belonged to the Chipenda faction of the MPLA.

A member of our party tried to escape, but when he was caught he said that he was only going to relieve himself. The gang told him that he would soon have all the time in the world to relieve himself for they would kill him; but the chief of the village, who had seven wives and fifteen children threatened the gang with witchcraft if they spilt blood in his village. They released us instantly, except for the pair of platform shoes that my brother-in-law was carrying.

When we crossed the Zambian border, three months after we set out, there were eleven of us left. I spent the rest of my childhood in Zambia. While there, I received a letter from a man in Huambo who had helped me when I was knocked down by a Portuguese taxi-driver. He asked me to send him a pair of shoes because it was impossible to find any in Angola. Afterwards he wrote to thank me for the shoes, but said they had arrived a bit late. Both his legs had been blown off in a land-mine explosion.

Waking in The Dark
by Rabun Belengaz (Kurdistan)

Waking in the dark. Where am I?
The rows of heads in this cavern
like Caron's load, no. Turning I
lift the window's plastic curtain,
frames a sunrise of orange peels.
I remember now, how the wheels

left the tarmac, felt the speed rope
my spine, and as the plane hoisted
itself dragged up, detached and snap,
no strings attached, I was released.
Waking in another belly.
leaving home (a relief really).

feeling a bit like Ulysses,
repeating, it little profits
that an idle king among these
barren crags, for me barren streets.
Streets I stalked hungry for the flesh
of misery, to suffer for fresh

images. Now thousands of feet
above the Atlantic, the plane
a Yeatsian swan, another street,
makes its way for the sphere's northern
parts, where I eagerly wait, for
a new constellation of stars.

Time
by Abdirahman Mirreh (Somalia)

How time changes
we fly with jumbo-jet Nairobi to Paris.

Cantata are tearing,
melting my soul,
did Bach dream of it
Cypress — picture from
Van Gogh, I admire your
resistance on the lonely
fields against the autumn wind.

Children....pariah dogs
barking in the distance of
the night, dead is the Tasmanian
race, his ghost appearing
in the tall acacia tree — the
twilight is blue.

Flying bird, cold aluminium,
with all that speed, how I do
hate your gleaming wings.

Road to Freedom
by Diangitukwa Fweley (Zaire)

observe this glowing brasier
it is time to depart
for freedom found under other skies
from the depths of solitude
towards the mountain heights

observe the sand trembling
life draws to a close
it is time to depart
in the distant silence
to search for understanding

hopefully they'll fade away-
these sighs of fear
life bereft of poetry
road paved with anguish
repulsive, barren heart

it is time to depart
for lasting peace
freedom fulfilled
along the paths of ancient truths
in this citadel of sublime soaring

(Translated by Jennifer Langer)

In Hiding
by Zuhair Al-Jazairi (Iraq)

I chronicled time in my diary step by step. But how to return from the sunny Alamawi courtyard scattered with pigeons, to my hiding place there? I will make a beginning of these events. It was when through prior arrangement, I met a man who seemed in haste; he moved and spoke rapidly like a bird. He placed the false passport in front of me saying briefly: "As from now, you are no longer who you are. Forget who you are and assume your new identity. You are a Jordanian merchant by the name of Nadhim Kamal, passing through by chance and in a hurry, huh?" He did not look at me as he spoke, nor did he wait for me to ask anything, but continued, pointing as he did so, to a page in the passport: "The task is quite simple, just sign and write the date here in this triangle and place your trust in God".

I examined the passport many times. I wanted to feel the delicate fingers that had made it and placed my picture on it. Happy and yet scared, I was now in possession of the instrument of my salvation or possible downfall. This passport put an end to my hesitation and delays and left me with one route to take, a risky one. As I turned the pages, I also wondered about the cruel, doubting eyes that would be examining it at the checkpoint. The guard would slowly come up to me to make the fatal statement: "That is not you!" However, I warded off this possibility with an irrevocable decision. "What does it matter? Hiding is a greater risk!"

In this new, secluded house on the edge of Baghdad, time was a burden which was painful and humiliating. Every morning the couple would leave for work saying their goodbyes to me with some pity. I read and read, my mind deranged by the multitude of words and depravity of life. Like a caged animal tormented by the need for space, I roamed the rooms of the house. Every other minute, I opened the fridge to eat or drink but not out of hunger or thirst. I smoked and drank coffee endlessly and later on would stand under the shower to calm my nerves. On television I watched the series "The Boat of Love", a paradise which enticed me. I was a prisoner of the secluded house and of the concept with which I had conspired to create another life.

When the wife returned from work, I welcomed her with overwhelming joy; there was a human being to talk to. I asked her with great persistence about news from the outside world. I was a victim of confinement and illusion imagining many things going on in this city where I was hiding. However, I was saddened by her boring interests; she neither read the newspapers nor was concerned with politics. "What do you expect to happen, other than that the price of eggs has gone up and the New Zealand meat has arrived?" Her husband returned home exhausted bearing a bottle of Arak and always starting his conversation with the remark "People are almost exploding with impatience". I was content with this feeble remark. It crystallised my illusions.

Every now and again the owner of the house received "unsafe" friends. I would then disappear to another room with a novel. However, my attention was diverted from the pages of the book as I found myself ashamedly eavesdropping on people who were unaware that the walls had ears listening to their passive conversation. They discussed the recent football match and real and fictitious sexual adventures during their recent visit to Poland. With nervous pleasure I listened to the voice of this friend I used to meet frequently when I was "alive". He sounded more coarse to me. I could not see his face but could imagine his eyes protruding whenever he was involved in serious discussion. Their conversations were fleeting and constantly changing, not allowing room for silence, as if through words they were hiding something horrible within themselves. I felt their voices become hoarse with fright when the discussion moved to me. One of them spoke of his last encounter with me and my son at the market, but I could not recall such a meeting. Another fabricated a lie to invigorate the discussion. A third alleged he had seen me the day before my arrest, torture and probable death, while I lay there hiding behind the walls. I smiled in disbelief that the person they were referring to was me.

Before leaving, I began to practise the role of the new identity I had assumed with my new passport. During my roaming in the house where I was hiding, again and again I would stand in front of the mirror, staring at the tense veins in my face, which had become more sullen and gaunt. My voice hissed: "You are not you, you are a Jordanian merchant named Nadhim Kamal!" I bit my lips to take a grip on the rebellious scream within me, against this self-denial. I drank Arak and read a poem by Elaur. The broken being emerged intact but hypersensitive and with tearful eyes. "You are me, why deny it?" Again I repeated the exercise, I roamed the house with steady steps like that of a determined man and within weeks I was wearing my mask: a moustache I had grown, a shaven head and the narrowing of my eyes to fit the dark, medical glasses. I had trained my voice to speak with the accent of a Jordanian Palestinian and simplified my words to suit the style of a salesman eager to persuade a customer. As I took on the role of the other person, my face became more pale and gaunt. I noticed as I stood in front of the mirror to chase away what remained of me. "Remember well. You are not you!"

When the date of my departure had been determined, I left my hiding place for the city. For the first time I joined the stream of workers heading for work. I wore an old, grey jacket and carried "his" briefcase, with a packet of cigarettes in my pocket and I imitated "his" cautious walk when I crossed the road. Yet I committed the first error of a man in hiding. I was unaware that during my absence, the road had been made one-way.

When night fell, I entered the house of some friends who were horrified to see me — a dead man brought back to

50

life. We drank, chatted and laughed to delay the horror that awaited us. The strong alcohol had liberated the frightened man hiding behind the mask of a Jordanian merchant and level-headed worker. I emerged reddened, angry and sarcastic to announce to my reflection in the mirror "I am no-one but myself!"

A Song for the Departure of Siyamand (excerpt)
by Kamal Mirawdeli (Kurdistan)

It scares me when the end of time
Tolls the bell of the call for separation
When a black shadow
Engulfs the last halo of your sight

I am scared of a time when like a madman
I look around in all directions
I look nearby, I look faraway
Except for the flame of a red sorrow
On the horizon, I can detect nothing

I am scared of a time..
The time has come
The wind of departure has blown
Load your luggage
Wither the last bud of a smile
Close your eyes with a sad heart
And say, "Goodbye love."

I am far away, you are far away
The roads are closed
Trees mourn their roots.

Hey, here is a henna party for your wedding!
Nay, it is the blood of dreams crimsoning horizons!

Prison and Torture

The Doves
by Reza Baraheni (Iran)

outside doves perch everywhere
it is clear from
their cooings of love and delight
it is clear from
the whirr of their wings
wings which seem to fan me in my prisoner's sleep
it is clear outside
doves perch everywhere

the night is like day on the other side of the bars
on this side the day is like night

Doctor Azudi, The Professional

Reza Baraheni (Iran)

Azudi is just like
Genghis Khan when he walks
he walks on a pile of fresh corpses

the Khan did not clean his teeth either
the Khan also belched the Khan
did not take off his boots either Azudi
has shattered the mouths of twenty poets today

Azudi wears a tie something
Genghis Khan never did
only this splendid detail reveals the prodigious march of
history

White Rock (excerpt)
by Ghazi Rabihavi (Iran)

The photographer jumped down over the gallows and his three cameras jumped around with him. We were worried something might happen to them. The gallows were still lying on the floor of the pick-up truck. He dusted off his trousers and said:

"Are you kids from around here?"

We looked at each other and one of us said:

"Are you going to take pictures of us or the dead man?"

The photographer blinked nervously and asked:

"Is he dead?" and ran, complete with the solid looking black cameras, to the patrol car. It had arrived with these three persuaders carrying G-3 guns about an hour earlier. And one us had said:

"I bet those guns aren't loaded."

Two of the officers threw their guns onto the back seat of the car and walked over to the pick-up. And one of us had said then:

"I bet those guns are loaded."

They began to help take out the gallows posts from the truck and to set them up on either side of the white rock where they had already dug two shallow holes to support them. Before they had found the rock, one of the *pasdars* had asked us:

"Hey, you. Can any of you get us a stool?" and one of us had said:

"He's going to be hanged, isn't he. Because you have to hang him."

But the other guy said:

"Don't bother with a stool: this white rock will do."

A few local men were coming our way from different parts of the town. It was a good Friday morning for a hanging, only it would have been even better if it hadn't started to snow, or if we'd had gloves. They said if it snowed they wouldn't hang him. It wasn't snowing when they brought the dead man. When they brought him he was alive.

He came out of the ambulance and sniffed the air. He had pulled up the zipper of his grey and green jumper — or someone had done it up for him because his hands were strapped behind his back. The first snowflakes settled on his hair. A group of locals ran towards him. The photographer was checking out his cameras. The headlights of the ambulance had been left on. The snowflakes were light and soft. They melted even before they touched the lights. One of us said:

"Pity. I wasn't even born when they executed the Shah's guard." One of us answered:

"My brother was born then; my dad sat him up on his shoulders so he could see the guy being executed. Bang! Bang!"

The truck driver said:

"I'd love to stay and watch. It'd mean a blessing for me. But I've got to deliver this food for the troops." The fat *pasdar* scratched his beard with the gun barrel and said:

"Good luck." The truck driver ran to the pick-up cursing the snow.

The prisoner was pacing up and down in the snow without any idea that he was moving closer and closer to the gallows. Sometimes he just stood there, with his long, thin legs, turning his head this way and that, sniffing the air. He wrinkled his nose and waggled his eyebrows, trying to shift the blindfold to find out where he was. But the blindfold was too tight. One of us said:

"Shout out his name so he knows where he is." Another said:

"When I used to know his name he was a different person."

A couple of people were still working on trying to get the gallows firm in the ground. Only men and children could come to watch. One of the guys, who had been given a leg up on the cupped hands of another, jumped down and said:

56

"Where's the other one?" The prisoner turned his head and said:

"Yeah. Where is he?" We didn't know the other guy; he wasn't from our town. We only saw him once — no, it was twice — on the same night. It was the beginning of autumn. The sun was just setting when we saw him entering the gates. He had a long turtle-neck sweater pulled down over his trousers. His clothes were black; like his hair. The officer on the gate was eating meat and rice. The stranger was carrying a bouquet of pink roses, and he was trying to hide a black plastic bag underneath it. He didn't like us watching him. But we did anyway and worked out that there were two bottles in the bag. He had the address of the prisoner but didn't know which way to go. So we showed him. At first, we thought he was a rather tall boxer. He ran his fingers through his hair and lifted his head. Then he looked down at us from under his eyelids. His eyebrows were shaved across his nose where they should have run together and he smiled at us. The sun trembling through the plane tree splashed his face with light and shade. He smiled and turned in the direction we had pointed. The security guy was washing his plate under the tap and asked us:

"Who was that?" and we told him. He looked over to the prisoner's house.

People were moving closer to the gallows, gathering in front of it. The photographer was sitting in the ambulance having a smoke. The prisoner, walking towards the gallows, was still unaware of where he was. One of the guards took his arm and pulled him over to the rock. The photographer grabbed his cameras and jumped out of the ambulance. He was wearing one of those safari vests with a lot of pockets. He got out a wire contraption from one of them and hooked them onto the shoulder tabs. Then he got out some white cloth and stretched it over the frame he had made. Now the snow wouldn't bother him. He ran across to the gallows with the umbrella that had sprouted from his shoulder.

None of the spectators were related to the prisoner; we didn't know if he had any relations. He was a loner; he built the wooden bodies for stringed instruments and twice a week went out of town. People said he had a wife and children somewhere that he had abandoned. The grocer had said to him:

"Give it another chance. You're only 45. It's just the right time to get married." The prisoner had smiled and said:

"Just the right time."

The guy holding onto the prisoner's arm was still looking at the hanging rope. Then he told the prisoner:

"Stand on top of this stone, will you, pal. Just to test everything's OK."

The prisoner's feet searched for the stone. Found it. If we could have seen his eyes, we could have told if he was frightened or not. That midnight, in the autumn, when the guards attacked his house and arrested both of them, he pressed his face against the rear window of the car, his eyes searching everywhere for his lover. Then, his voice trembling, he yelled from behind the glass:

"Leave him alone!" The car drove off; a crushed pink rose was still sticking to the back tyre.

The prisoner asked:

"Is it time?" The *pasdar* said:

"No. The *hadji* hasn't arrived yet. We can't start without him." He said:

"Then what?" The officer said: "Take your shoes off. This is only a trial run." The prisoner took his bare feet out of the loose-fitting canvas shoes and stood on them. His long, thin toes were red with cold. They had up-ended the white rock and were holding it in position; the slightest kick would topple it, leaving his feet dangling in space.

"Now climb up." He put one foot on the rock. It shifted, swayed, nearly fell over. The guard jumped forward and set it straight again.

"What's with you? Are you in a hurry?" he said. Then he got up and one by one, carefully placed the prisoner's feet

58

on the stone. The prisoner stood on the stone and was raised up above the crowd.

Notes:
Pasdar is a revolutionary guard.
Hadji is a mullah.

Punishment

by Ahmad Shamloo (Iran)

In this place there is a maze of prisons
And in each prison a myriad of dungeons
And in each dungeon countless cells
And in each cell scores of men in irons

One, amongst these men
Persuaded of his wife's infidelity
Plunged his dagger deep

Another, amongst these men
Desperate to put bread in his children's mouths
Slaughtered, in the searing summer mid-day heat

Some, amongst these men
On a deserted rainy day
Ambushed the money lender

Others, in the quiet of the alley
Crept stealthily on to roofs

Still others
Plundered gold teeth from fresh graves
At midnight

But I, I have never murdered on a dark and stormy night
But I, I have never ambushed a money lender
But I, I have never crept stealthily on to roofs

In this place there is a maze of prisons
And in each prison a myriad of dungeons
And in each dungeon countless cells
And in each cell scores of men in irons   .

Amongst these men in irons
Are those
Who can only come
With dead women

Amongst these men in irons
Are those
Who in their dreams see the final scream
Of the woman they have strangled
But I, I never seek anything in a woman
Unless — unexpectedly, serenely
She's there — my soulmate

But I, deep in my reveries, I
Don't lend an ear except to
The distant echo of a persistent strain
Of desert grass which
Sprouts
Shrivels
Withers
And scatters in the wind

But I, if I were not a man in irons
One dawn
Like a faraway, elusive memory
I would have transcended this cold, contemptible place

This
Is my crime

(Translated from Farsi by Ahmad Ebrahim and Karina Zabihi)

The Shah's Executioner
by Reza Baraheni (Iran)

The pistol in the hand of the tall, bearded, young man was
aimed at me when I pulled down the car window after I
came to the stop light at the end of Queen Elizabeth
Boulevard. It was a dirty day, a dirty crossroad and the
dirtiest hour of the blazing sun of Teheran, and the young
man's complexion was no less dirty. But he was recklessly
cool. When he lifted his dark glasses to his sweating forehead with his left hand, he did not bother at all about the
cars hooting in all directions and the people rushing to the
scene, to where its armed protagonist was standing in the
open sun sweating.

"If you make a move, I'll blow your brains out," he said
through yellowing teeth. He thrust his hand inside the
car, opened the door expertly and sat by my side with the
pistol still pointed at my ribs. "Move on and stop on the
other side." "But who are you?" I asked as soon as I could
ask questions, although I could already guess. "I am an
agent of SAVAK," he mumbled, "and you have to come
with us." The people had already disappeared, seeing the
pistol, and the cars moved as naturally as if nothing had
happened. I stopped the car on the other side, and then I
saw three people in a car parked ahead of me. One of
them leaped out and ran towards my car, opened the driver's door, and pushing me forward against the steering
wheel, settled himself in the back seat. I knew that he
also had a pistol in his hand. The man at the steering
wheel in the other car opened the door, came out, and
turned to us shouting: "Let's go and inspect his house."
And then, turning to me in particular, he said in the most
sarcastic tone I had heard in my life: "Behave yourself,
Professor." The word "professor", which I had never
used in my academic career, used now by this man from
the Secret Police, sounded like a divine curse in my ears.
My wife, my tiny brother-in-law and my parents-in-law

were waiting for me at the top of the stairs when I went up with three of the four following me. I winked at my wife, telling her: "We have guests." "But why didn't you say so?" protested my wife. "I thought we were all going to eat out." The men could not wait for any explanation on my part. We went in. One of the men closed the door and the inspection of the house started right away while everybody watched.

They knew what they were doing. In less than an hour, they had turned the whole flat into a pile of garbage heaped in the middle of the rooms. Even our bedroom. And even children's toys were torn apart and inspected. The better educated of the three, the driver, went through all the shelves of the Persian books, picking out one here and another there, and putting them on the desk. When they finished, the flat was like a house after an earthquake or an air raid.

"Let's go," said the driver to me after he had successfully identified himself to us as the leader. My wife wanted to say something in protest, but she gave up as soon as she saw the helplessness in my eyes. I wanted to have time to think, and also give my wife all the money I had with me.

"Are you sure I'm the man you are looking for?" I asked. "What do you mean?" asked the leader. "Nothing. I simply wanted you to know that there's another Dr Baraheni besides me." They wouldn't bother to go after my elder brother, who was a Professor of Psychology in the University of Teheran. He was a quiet man and had never said or written anything against the authorities.

The man spoke into his walkie-talkie. I took the money out of my pocket and handed it to my wife. "Your first name is Reza, isn't it?" "Yes," I said. He spoke into his walkie-talkie again: "We have got the 'project.' We'll be there pretty soon." I was their 'project.' He turned to me: "It's you we want. Let's go." Then he looked at my wife. "Madam," he said, "we'll bring the Professor back in two hours." Nobody said a word. We went down the stairs in a hurry. We got in the car, their car this time. They blindfolded me after we had driven for some time. Now I only knew that we were driving to the centre of the city. It took us about an hour. How could I be back home in an hour or two?

They took everything away from me. When they blindfolded me again, I had no belt, no shoe laces, no socks, no handkerchief, no pen, pencil or paper. They also made a list of the books they had taken from my flat and forced me to sign a statement saying that these dangerous books belonged to me. Then I was taken out again, pushed through several doors, all iron, and finally we seemed to have arrived at our destination. I was told, "put your foot up, put your foot down," each time we went through a door. The final door opened with the pulling of bolts and a hammer-like sound. I was pushed in, the blindfold was removed and I found myself in what I was later to learn was Dungeon No. 14.

I was still a fool, thinking that they couldn't do this to me, that they would come any minute to apologise for what they had done. But subsequent events proved that I too, like my nation, had been taught to believe in miracles. They came in and took me out, blindfolded and handcuffed, and again we passed through several iron doors. Finally, when they took the handkerchief away, I was facing a man who told me to sit down and answer his questions. I was accused of having relations with the Confederation Of Iranian Students Abroad. I denied the accusation. All this time I had been hearing noises, all kinds of noises, people screaming and asking for help, and others swearing at the tops of their voices, and the sound of whips and clubs being swung and the moaning of men and women everywhere. Where was I? And I actually went ahead and asked the man where I was. "None of your business, you son of a bitch," the man shouted. "Here the questions come from us, not from traitors like you!" And there were all sorts of questions dealing with my entire life, with the emphasis laid on the last twenty years, my whole literary career. The guard was ordered to take me back to my cell. I was blindfolded and handcuffed again and taken back to the dungeon.

It was a four foot by eight foot hole with nothing on the ancient tiles. The light shone in through a small window barred on both sides. The shouting was actually coming from all over the place. It seemed as if a great religious procession was moving on all the floors. The sound of whispering, rather indiscreet for this sort of situation, came from the other cells. Sometimes there would be loud moaning or sobbing, and generally when the iron door of the block was opened and shut, there would come wailing and crying. Nothing except prison sounds could be heard. Next night, I was to join the ranks of the doomed, underground wailers and mourners. I put my jacket under my head as a pillow and tried to go to sleep. But thoughts of outside and the screams of inside wouldn't let me. In less than six hours I had been disconnected from the rest of the world like a nobody, like a termite on the verge of being squeezed and trampled by anonymous forces. The world had thrust out its hidden bowels and swallowed me up. But somehow, everything seemed like a bad dream, a dirty joke, an allegory, the meaning of which, one cannot grasp, except through allusions and inferences, and when the moaning is about to be disclosed, one collapses under its looming ugliness, or simply ceases to exist.

I believe I had just closed my eyes, when suddenly the door was flung open with a snapping and banging that sent me springing from the floor to the door. It was morning. I hadn't realised it. Days come and go in prison without the prisoner becoming conscious of the light of day. A new guard was standing in front of me with the blindfold hanging from his shoulder. "Get up," he said, "and put your shoes on." I was taken out blindfolded and handcuffed. I was aware, through the blindfold, of the faint light of the sun. When I was being taken through the courtyard, I heard somebody shout in an imperious voice:

"Bring that son of a cuckold here!" I was pushed into a room and the blindfold was removed. There was a group of

65

people in suits and ties, and several others in sweaters, and then several others with blindfolds and handcuffs. These last people couldn't stand properly. They seemed to be suffering from something in their shoulders, legs, feet, heads and hands.

"You see this son of a cuckold? He is much more dangerous than all the terrorists, the communists, the Fedaeyeen, and the socialists. It's because of this son of a bitch that we have all these cells full of students. They are all his students. This pimp is responsible for all the people in all our prisons. You cuckold, how dare you write those things against the government? Is it a pen you are holding in your hand or a spade? What is it that turns you into a howling beast in the Iranian press? Isn't a university professorship enough for you? Your father was a porter in the bazaars of Tabriz! Didn't this present government educate you so that you could become a professor? What else do you want, you son of a bitch?"

The man saying these words was bald, very well dressed, and his eyes were so nervous and red that I thought a few other sentences from him, and he would find his eyes leaping out of their sockets and falling on the floor at his feet. Before he finished the last sentence, he took long, hurried and nervous steps towards me and started slapping me on the face. It seemed that he could not stop himself from shouting when he was slapping. There was total harmony between the two actions: "What the hell is the matter with you? What's this beard you have grown? You want to look like a terrorist leader? I'll spit on this beard of yours, and when we get rid of you, I'll come personally and shit on your grave. Didn't I shit on Al-Ahmad's grave? Well, I'll come and shit on your grave too!"

I wanted to find a minute of time and explain a few things, but he wouldn't give me a chance. He was busy using his hands on my face and his feet on my lower parts, swearing at me and my whole family, in particular my wife and daughter, my mother and sister. When he was tired he turned to the guard who had brought me to him: "Go and get someone to shave his beard." The man arrived, but I later found out that he was not the barber. He was a short blue-eyed man who was the prison nurse and was called "Doctor" by the prisoners. He was a pitiless man who wouldn't even give them an aspirin. He had no razors available to shave me. The bald man wouldn't take no for an answer. He slapped me twice more and ordered the man to shave me with scissors. The man took a pair of surgical scissors from his sack, led me to the side of the pool, sat me down and started cutting my beard. Whenever his tiny scissors were not a match for my thick and long beard, he would virtually pull out the hair out very hard with the ends of the scissors. Then I heard the bald man shout from the room: "Take the cuckold into Otagh-e Tamshiyat!" I had never heard of this combination of words, half Turkish and half Arabic. Literally it would mean: the room in which you make people walk, but I soon found out that it actually meant the torture chamber. I was blindfolded again and led by two of the guards, one on each side, up a long flight of stairs. When I was on the third floor, I was forced to pass through something which resembled a leather-made curtain or perhaps a tunnel. This was used for mystification purposes. The prisoner would be kept in the dark all the time. The curtains led to an iron door, too small even for my size. In fact I didn't think it was a room at first. The leather-made tunnel, the small iron door and the blindfold gave me the feeling that I was going to be buried alive. So tight and narrow and suffocating did everything seem that I was already gasping for breath. The order came from a metallic voice: "Take the blindfold off." One of the guards untied the blindfold, and I found myself surrounded by four other men in addition to the guards.

Note:
Jalal Al-Ahmad was a writer who died in mysterious circumstances.

Conversation at the Bend in the Road
by Buland al-Haidari (Iraq)

Haven't you slept... sad guard,
When do you sleep?
You, who have not known sleep in the light of our lamp for
a thousand years
You, who have been crucified between his outstretched
palms for years,
Don't you ever sleep?
— For the twentieth time... I want to sleep
I fall asleep but can never sleep
For the fiftieth time
I fell asleep and couldn't sleep
For sleep to the sad guard
Remains like the edge of a knife
I'm afraid of sleeping
I'm afraid of waking to dreams.

Let them burn Rome... let them burn Berlin
Let them steal the Wall of China
You have to sleep...
It's time this sad guard
Had a rest for a moment... he sleeps
— I sleep... and Berlin burns every second
And every hour a wall is stolen from China
Between one blink and another a dragon is born
I'm afraid of sleeping
For sleep to the sad guard
Remains like the edge of a knife
        ...I'm afraid of sleeping
  For sleep to the sad guard
  Remains like the edge of a knife.

Poem to a Prison Companion
by Cikuru Batumike (Zaire)

Indeed, I will hear no more the Masai drums
At night, no more will the cock, the hen, the cow
be my companions
It will be long before I come upon them again
my creator, equal of God
I will see no more my comforting mother
nor will I hear the other's cries
pulled by her chained feet
Her body dragged there on the stairs
lying inert face down
I will see her no more
hear her no more
Screaming with pain and anger
grasping for a hand to extricate her from the hole
Prisoners
We will sing together no more
to evoke the protection of the Lord
But it is no longer distant
That great day which will come
When you too will challenge hatred and its cohort
And those others will slide down the slippery slope.

(Translated by Jennifer Langer)

Women's Experiences

Through the Vast Halls of Memory 1
by Haifa Zangana (Iraq)

Pointing to the last cell at the end of the corridor, the guard said in a loud voice:

"There is barely any room left for more prisoners. You must stay with Um Wahid, Um Jassim and Um Ali".

Slowly I followed the big woman's steps. She was in her forties. Her hair was jet-black and her body a huge mass of fat that vibrated with every step; buttock up, the rest of her body down, left, right. I did not know what to do with my right hand. I kept trying to adjust the strap of my handbag, but then realised I was not even carrying one. I put my hands in the pockets of my navy blue skirt, took them out, put them back in. Slowly I followed the guard's steps. She was wearing a grey uniform. The walls were concrete, the floor concrete, the ceiling concrete. Were the women too made of the same substance?

The front of each cell was made of iron bars with a door on the right-hand side. There were two rows of cells with iron bars facing each other. The corridor was a metre wide. To maintain some privacy, the women had used old, grey blankets as curtains, knotted to the bars in the most bizarre ways.

Many eyes stared at me, the eyes of women with their bodies wrapped in black clothes. The whole place was in black and grey, like an old photo from a family album. The women's faces were a funny colour, not pale in the usual way, the pallor of illness and fatigue. In their faces, I beheld the dryness and cracking of earth that has suffered drought for many years. The concrete floor did not nourish seeds, the light bulbs surrounded by wire did not give light.

The guard stopped at the last cell and told the three prisoners: "This is the new prisoner. She's a political." She pronounced that slowly and firmly as if introducing a new breed of animal and then she slowly left.

I did not know what to do, so I stood where I was, hoping one of them would make the first move. The cell was a cube with a small barred window looking onto another concrete wall a few metres away. In the right-hand corner, there was a cubicle big enough to accommodate one person sitting or standing. In it was a tap and a flask. It was the toilet, the bathroom, the place where the three women could wash their cutlery, clothes and their bodies. The two walls of the cubicle were so low, they barely covered the lower part of the body. The entrance was decorated with an old cotton night-dress.

For years, the women had continued cutting up old blankets and clothes for use as curtains, hanging them up in the afternoon when the prison warden left, and taking them down in the morning before she arrived for inspection. With endless determination, they persisted in the same ritual, as if proving to themselves and the others that, in enjoying some privacy, they could still defy the system.

It was evening. One of the women, the smallest one, with long plaits, was wearing a black, long-sleeved dress over striped pyjamas. She carried her mattress on her head and walked out of the cell, staggering under the heavy load. The second woman did the same. She was very old, wrinkled, with gums that made unusual sounds. Her wrinkled face was covered in tattoos. The blue tattoos began at her eyebrows and continued to her navel, as she later proudly showed us. Was she in her eighties? She carried her mattress on her head and left. The third woman stood next to me:

"Do you have a mattress?"

"Have you any clothes apart from what you're wearing?" She peered at my face, particularly my chin covered in sores. Then she put her mattress on her head and indicated to me to follow her.

"My name is Um Wahid. The little woman is Um Jassim. She's sentenced to fifteen years. Old Um Ali will be released in two years. The warden lets us sleep in the yard because it's impossible to sleep inside because of this heat."

I sat down on the mattress Um Wahid had lent me. Um Wahid was the longest serving prisoner in the women's prison. She had been sentenced to life along with her brother. They had murdered her husband together. Shortly after their wedding, he had treated her badly, beating her up and forcing her to entertain his friends. One morning, while her husband was at work, she had packed her bags and left, returning to her family in the south. Her mother had sent her back straightaway, saying. "Your home now is with your husband. We don't want you anymore."

Her uncle accompanied her to Baghdad. Um Wahid told her young brother that her husband was forcing her to be a prostitute. Together they agreed the only solution was to kill him. So they killed him. At the time she was nineteen and her brother seventeen. Over the years, Um Wahid had accumulated many aluminium plates, pans, spoons, pillows, clothes and blankets. Being there for such a long time, she was the official recipient of the prisoners' leftovers, the things they did not want to take with them on release, reminders of prison.

My bed was next to Um Jassim's in the concrete yard surrounded by a high barbed wire fence. My continual coughing drove someone to complain. I heard one of them say:

"Maybe she's suffering from TB."

At that moment, and for no good reason (maybe it was the sympathy shown by Um Wahid, the other women's silence, or the complaints some of them made), the mask I had worn for some weeks now began to crack. The mask had protected me from seeing, smelling, touching, but not from hearing. Hearing the voices of the tortured, trying to recognise their identities, hearing the torturers' footfall in the corridors of the Qasir, listening to the sound of keys turning in locks, trying to identify the last click before the torturer would appear before me. I touched my dishevelled hair, matted with dirt and dried blood. I smelt the odour of my body, touched my hair, my face and cried. I cried quietly, a painful, continuous moaning that lasted all night, during which I mourned my disappointments, my fear and the longing I had to see my friends and comrades. Can the soul be separated from its shell and leave it behind to wander the open fields?

I gaze into the darkness. I see a green mountain, heavy with bushes and cypress trees. At its foot are vineyards, overlooking a village. The tinkling of water can be heard inside the houses. I see a group of children picking up camomile leaves, putting them in cotton bags, competing with each other to fill them up. I see them eating figs on their way home, and throwing walnuts at each other. I see myself laughing happily with them.

A Story, A Tale
by Dieudonnée-Marcelle Makenga (Zaire)

At last I am going there
to the country of liberty

I have read the guides
on the country of liberty
the pictures, the dreams
will become reality
at last liberty
no more nightmares
I will be able to breathe freely

I am there, my Lord, I am there
everything is delightful, everything is beautiful
better than in my wildest dreams
Never have I seen anything like it
everything is novel
the land of wonders
like no other
definitely unlike the one I left behind
nothing here is the same
I just have to settle in

It won't take long
I just need to wait a little
I am a foreigner so must be patient
I will end up being happy
they are not all nasty
as my people here say
despite the sniggering and jeering
they will finally give me

my papers

It should not be long
in the meantime I can't do anything
there is nothing to be done
other than go round in circles
and watch the others
pretending to be happy
when I arrive here

"papers"

That's all I hear
throughout the day
It's unending
when I reach here

So I remain isolated
and in my head the insults
the abuse resound
I am

a foreigner

They insult me, are aggressive
in my head despair
point the finger of scorn at me
I am trapped like a deer
my dreams disintegrate
I never imagined it
I believed I would lead a good life

I believed those guides
I had read about it in books
glossy magazines
they had deceived me

Now I am awake
it was only a nightmare
the land of wonders
was only an ugly story

papers

(Translated by Jennifer Langer)

Child of Exile
by Munzur Gem (Kurdistan)

*The subject matter of this story derives from an event that
took place among a group of Kurds sent into exile to Turkish western regions, at the time of the 1938 Dersim mas-
sacre.*

The people who filled the railway truck were startled as
the door creaked shut with a grating noise. Their eyelids
flickered, and they sought one another's tired and feeble
gaze, but in vain, for everything was instantly lost, buried
in darkness.

Then, accompanied by a long whistle, and hissing
sharply, the truck began to move. And with that, the last
fragments of hope that had protected them till now vanished completely. Their hearts were heavy and sad, their
wits numbed as though bewitched, their bodies unable to
function. It was the melancholy and loss of morale which
had followed their abandonment of Elaziz after Dersim
which was turning the truck into a graveyard, and the
tears trickling down their cheeks and falling to the ground
also retained the silence of the graveyard.

Zeyne, hands clasped on her knees, was waiting motionless as though nailed to the wooden floor. She was so deep
in thought that she noticed neither movements around
her nor Fate's moaning beside her. She didn't even hear
the sighs of her old neighbour coughing repeatedly a little
way off. And her preoccupation continued until she felt a
hand pressing her arm. Recovering, she turned quickly
and looked but could not make out the owner of the hand.
Who was pressing her arm? she wondered. A little later
she asked softly:

"Who is it? Is there something you want to tell me?" "I
was the one who squeezed your arm. Zeyne abla." Fate
replied. "Ah, so it was you," said Zeyne, but there was no
need to ask the reason, for the voice and heavy panting

explained everything. Still, she bent down to look more closely. Now here eyes, used to the darkness, could distinguish some things although not very clearly. Fate's back leant against the wall, her legs stretched out before her and her hand on her belly. She was shuddering, biting her lips in pain, and her head kept rolling from side to side.

When Zeyne saw her condition she straightened up, lifted up her head and opened her hands wide:

"Dear God, don't do this to the poor woman. How can she give birth amongst so many people in this dark, filthy truck? Did you make a mistake? There isn't even a clean piece of rag to wrap up the baby. At least if she can only wait until she gets off the train," she begged. Then she turned to Fate again and laid her hand on her forehead, bathed in cold sweat. Fate's breathing came and went like a bellows. Zeyne was about to speak when the other stirred and said "Zeyne abla." "Yes." At that moment Fate held her hand tightly. "You know, I like you so much; you're just like an elder sister to me. Ever since I can remember we've been like sisters. You see how I am, Zeyne, I'm not well, I know it! This business will kill me. And to tell the truth I wouldn't care much, for death comes to us all, except for those two children.

If I die what do you think will happen to them? If only their father was alive, I wouldn't worry any more. What terrible luck that he's not alive. Curse the bullets that found their way to him and did nothing to us. But we all had to die there or leave. We couldn't possibly have lived with that grief and shame. If anything happens to me, I ask you to look after those two orphans. Promise me you won't abandon them," she said. When Zeyne heard her neighbour's words she struck her knee with her free hand: "Oh ho! Just look at this business! For heaven's sake, see what you've been saying — where did that word 'death' come from, Fate? It's going to be a topsy-turvy kind of birth, anyway, isn't it? Would the situation be any different if you'd been at home? I don't want to hear that kind of talk from you any more, Fate; OK?" she exclaimed.

"No matter what you say, I know what will happen."
"And I tell you, clear death completely out of your mind
and hang on to your morale. You'll see, everything will
turn out all right," replied Zeyne. "Apart from anything
else, Zeyne, won't I die of shame? How can a birth take
place before so many people? Wouldn't it be better for a
woman to die before such a thing could happen to her?"

In answer Zeyne clasped her hand tighter and caressed
Fate's hair as though petting a child. In fact what Fate had
said had some truth in it and the same things had occurred
to her. When she was waiting to be exiled, in the building
in Elaziz belonging to the military, her eyes had often
travelled between Fate's swollen belly and the Turkish
officers. She had kept hoping that one of them would say:
"Let's not send this woman who is about to give birth; let's
leave her till later," but her hope was unfulfilled and her
wish denied. And so now birth had arrived in the truck
and was suddenly knocking at the door. With these
thoughts, a lightning explosion flashed through her head
— her feelings were in revolt; then her lips trembled and
words poured out in a stream. "Is all this any fault of
yours, you unlucky woman? What wrong have you ever
done? Were you the one responsible for all the events?
What harm have you ever done to anyone? Did you tell the
soldiers 'Come in and set my house on fire and send me
into exile?' You never did anything to feel guilty about,
poor little woman."

Everyone heard what Zeyne was saying and the silence
in the truck grew even deeper. Those who knew of Fate's
plight acknowledged the truth of Zeyne's words, but those
further away were pondering the reasons for this harsh
outburst. But Fate's scream gave them their answer. Then
a shift took place in two directions. The women moved
nearer Fate, and the men moved further away, as far as
they could go. They were not satisfied with just moving
away but sat so that their backs were turned to her. Even
if the interior was dark and not much could be seen, this
made everyone comfortable. And the children made up a

80

third group. Some were waiting together silent as death; some were whispering to each other, some were laughing under their breath. But it was Fate's two children who were undoubtedly in the worst state. They clung to one another and waited. They didn't know whether they should grieve for their mother's pain, or find ways to avoid the mocking glances of some of the other children, or share in the excitement of their sibling's birth. They were confused by the many conflicting emotions in their hearts.

Minutes and hours succeeded each other like this; then a flurry of movement arrived among the women who had lifted Fate to her feet and, making a circle around her, walked her up and down, to and fro, moving and pausing. Now Zeyne was seen to break from the group and approach the men. Several people looked at her as if to inquire, "What is it? What do you want?" "The floor is very hard. If you could give up some of your outer garments we could spread them out and get her to lie down."

No one uttered a sound. Instead, hands and arms were busy and jackets and shawls were removed and handed to Zeyne, while Hacer was also doing the same amongst the women. And so all was ready and prepared for the birth and after it. But there were still difficulties, for the birth was not under way; neither an older woman's skilful hands, nor Fate's strenuous efforts nor prayers for a conclusion, were of any help, and time limped slowly on, burdened by increasing anxiety.

Long after, no one knew how long, Fate's screams were accompanied at last by the new sound of a baby's cry. Then everyone drew a deep breath and for the first time for days, faces were really smiling and eyes glistened.

While two of the women were busy with the baby, Zeyne knelt by Fate and wiped away her sweat, and tried to cool her by blowing on her. When Fate opened her eyes, Zeyne took the baby from Zere's arms and held it out to Fate.

"A beautiful little girl," she murmured.

As soon as Fate held the baby in her arms, the pain and weariness in her face immediately vanished and was replaced by profound joy as though she had never suffered all that pain. As she tried to get the child to suckle, on the other side, amongst the men, a discussion was going on about a suitable name for the child of exile.

Galti-Mucruuf

by Maxamed Daahir Afrax (Somalia)

The novel Galti-Mucruuf, *which offers a sharp social and political critique of the Somalia of the late 1970s, began to appear in serialised form in* The October Star *in 1980. However, the government suddenly discontinued its publication and muzzled its author who went into exile soon after.*

An episode from Camel Driver Politics (Galti-Macruuf) *a novel from Somalia. The story is set in the Mogadishu of the late 70s. The father of Shamis Cige drives her into prostitution by forcing her into an unwanted marriage with a man in his seventies.*

As he reached the spot where his daughter was sitting, he stopped and took off the thick glasses which the doctor had prescribed as his eyesight had begun to fail. "Shamis, haven't you gone to school today?" he said with an undertone of reproach. Before she answered, Shamis respectfully stood up. The calm voice in which her father asked the question and his use of her name rather than a direct reproach took her by surprise. That was not how she knew him. When she looked at his face, she was even more surprised, for she sensed from it a lightness and hidden pleasure she had not seen in a long time. "It must be quite something that has made my father happy this morning," she said to herself.

"Father, I did go, but they sent me away, both Rashid and myself, and they told us to bring our father."

"Why? What happened? Didn't I go to the principal? Didn't I tell him that, although I cannot buy uniforms for my children, he should let them stay in school anyway? What is this business of 'bring your father' everyday? Or have you done anything else wrong?"

"We have not done anything else wrong. They just want the uniform and the books. Every teacher who comes to class asks us about them."

83

"I will talk to the principal and you...."

"Father, this really is a problem. Please get us school clothes and books by any means. Only we have been given special consideration; the other students had their clothes and books in order last month. In my class I have to stand up every day. The principal told me: 'Last year we gave you special dispensation; this year you must come up with the uniform.' Father, I can't bear it that the other children look down on me everyday and that the girls of my age refer to me as 'that beggar.' As she said this, tears fell from the eyes she had covered with her hands and her voice broke.

For a while Cige stared at the ground and kept silent. The tearful words of his daughter burned in his heart and reopened an old wound. But cry he would not, whatever the pain in his heart. Whenever there was a problem he could not solve, he soothed his children saying: "Forget about it, my child. This is God's will, this is the fate that has been written for us."

Since they had been lenient with him several times, this year he had intended to come up with his children's school supplies. But where to get them? These 270 shillings that made up his wage, should he use them to stave off starvation and spend them on food which had gone sky high in price? Should he protect his children against having to go naked and being cold? Should he buy medicine for the child who got sick, or should he spend them on school supplies? From where else could he come up with something? His only hope had been to send someone to his brother to tell him to sell a few sheep from the livestock he still owned in the country-side, but that had proved to be impossible. The livestock had been killed off by drought, he had been told, and there was neither anything to sell nor anyone to buy! The very brother whom he had expected to sell some animals for him had himself sent a letter saying: "We are in the grip of a drought. Help us out with at least something!"

For two months he had struggled, and in the end he had succeeded in buying school supplies for his three youngest children who attended the primary and lower secondary schools. As for the two attending the higher secondary school, 'They are big,' he had said to himself, "and can be made to understand or I can inform their teachers." He had informed the principal in person and they had agreed that he should make some effort and provide the necessities for one child, in which case they would forgive him the rest. What could he tell the principal if he were to go and see him today? He shook his head. Then he remembered! The matter which had slipped his mind for a few minutes came back to him. It was the very thing that had made him look cheerful when he first arrived. All signs of worry disappeared from his face and his eyes twinkled with new hope. While Shamis dried her tears, he sat down next to her, put one arm around her shoulder and said in a loving voice: "You have nothing to cry about, daughter, I have good news for you!"

"Bless you, father, what is it?" she answered enthusiastically, as her face grew lively and full of anticipation. "After today you will never be dismissed from school again and your schoolmates will no longer look down on you." She got up and grabbed his knees with both hands as he had always done when she had asked him for something, even when she had been a small girl: "Father, have you found work for me?" "No, not work, but something even better," he answered full of confidence. She looked at him with doubtful, questioning eyes, but held back her words. She was afraid to articulate what she thought he meant. She begged God that her premonition would turn out to be false. When he saw that she held her question back, he gave her all the news: "A decent, wealthy man has asked for your hand, and I have given you to him."

It was as if something snapped inside her and suddenly froze; her heart pounded hard. She took her hands off his knees and sat down again. That her father would give her to a man she had not chosen and did not like was one of life's hardships she had often lamented; she begged God to spare her. She had often heard her father boast that he would give her away in marriage; that is what had caused her to fear this kind of thing. Her face and voice completely changed. "What kind of a man is this person?" she asked. "Xaaji Meecaad." "Who is this Xaaji Meecaad? Is it this old geezer who is the father of our Physics professor?" "That is him, but he is not as old as you think. He is a real prince and has a good reputation, which is why I have given you my blessing to marry him, my daughter. He is the God-sent solution to our financial problems and for you he will be good. As people said in the old days: "A man who is old enough to be a woman's father knows how to handle her."

The shock made her silent for a while. She hung her head and aimlessly drew lines in the sand. She thought of a number of things: to weep, to run away, to explode and throw ugly words at their father. All that occurred to her, but she was unable to move either her tongue or her legs and could not decide what to do or not to do. Her father could read on her face what she felt in her heart filled with unexpected grief. "Her refusal to co-operate may yet spoil your plan," he said to himself. He moved closer to her and said in a sweet, pleading voice: "Shamis, why aren't you speaking, dear daughter? Aren't you happy with that to which I have given my blessing and have chosen for you?" Speaking in one breath, as if she was reading from a book, Shamis said: "Father, if I have become too heavy a burden for you to bear, why don't you just send me away? Why do you burden me with an old man who is even older than yourself? We have lived in poverty all this time. Can't you tolerate that one year of school that I have left before I can go to work for you?" Her grief had made her unusually eloquent. Her choice of words pleased her and gave her some relief, and her father, surprised, fell silent in his turn.

Gige had anticipated that his daughter might be unhappy about the matter and even that she might refuse, but he had not expected her to speak like that. He had not thought that she would see herself as someone being sold or unloaded as a heavy burden. That sentiment really hurt the old man. Shamis had touched on another sore point: the efforts he had made to give her an education should not have to be sacrificed as the time to reap their fruits was so near. As this new thought occurred to him, he suddenly regretted the promise to Xaaji Meecaad and the cheque he had accepted from him. But what could he do now? Had he not given his word as a respectable elder? He must sweet-talk the girl into accepting. After all, he had not only given her away in marriage because of the money required. Wealth and reputation were all that mattered in the world, he believed. If she had found a husband who had both, plus the wisdom that comes with age, what else could she wish for? These days she was pursued by kids who were still wet behind the ears. Before they made off with her, he had concluded, he should tie her fate to that of the gentleman who had asked for her hand. As for her, he knew that she was a young girl who obeyed her father and never talked back. He was therefore confident that she would accept his decision, even if she was unhappy about it. She was decent and intelligent, and this way he could also be sure that her womanhood would not be blemished.

The Girl in the Rose Scarf
by Mojdeh Shahriari (Iran)

Gharghad Goli was sixteen years old and wore a new rose scarf bought for her on the occasion of her sister's wedding. The scarf complemented her beauty and accentuated the glow in her big eyes. Those eyes were characterised by a sorrowful grace that suited her lean, frail figure. When the guests wished her luck, she could not hide her excitement; an innocent smile erupted on her face.

The girl stayed at home. She would wash the tea glasses and saucers and then clean the house. Gloomily she would go outside and silently stare at the old decaying, cypress tree, the only tree they had in the yard. At first she thought she would soon get used to her sister's absence, but her melancholy got worse. She was isolated from the outside world. She stayed home and did the chores and sorely missed her sister's companionship.

That day she was thinking about her sister more than ever. She tried to hold back her tears. She wept in silence for a while, then shook herself and remembered that she was supposed to be preparing stewed beef and beans for dinner. She felt slightly better. At least for a few minutes, while she was at the market, she could see some people. She decided to wear her rose scarf. She had not used it since her sister's wedding because she wanted to have it for special occasions. But now she needed to feel its beauty and feel the pride of her shoulders beneath it. She carefully folded it into two equal triangles, took the ends in her hands, set the scarf on her thin, black, curly hair and gently tied the ends together under her chin into a firm knot. Then she rushed to the mirror, looked at her head from all angles, and stared at her image with satisfaction for a few minutes. She was elated. She was thinking that as soon as she stepped outside, everyone would stare at her admiringly. She removed a twenty toman note from inside the sacred book of Zoroaster and ran outside.

She saw some of the neighbourhood women in the greengrocer's shop. Most of them were Zoroastrians. She greeted them as she passed them. Then she furtively turned round to look at them. They paid no attention to her. Perhaps they had not noticed her rose scarf at all. Or maybe they had noticed it but decided to ignore her out of envy. What if they were making fun of her now? But Gharghad Goli did not want to be pessimistic. She told herself "I'm probably imagining it." But behind her back, in the circle of the women, the whispering had already begun: "Did you see how the little devil had made herself up?" "She looks as if she were on her way to a wedding party!" "Maybe she is up to something, her own wedding perhaps!"

But Gharghad Goli was happy. She did not feel depressed any more. She stopped to look at every little shop, store and sidewalk stand. Even the fight between two little boys rolling over in the dirt, hurling insults at each other and tearing each other's shirts, was amusing to her. She wished she could spend all the time on the street. She wished these damned houses did not exist at all. She hated their own small house and adored the streets, alleys, stores, people, even the stray dogs. Even the dry, annoying heat of the desert outskirts would not detract from this love of the outside world... The shouts of a woman scolding her son detracted from her thoughts: "God damn you Mahmoud, it's almost noon. Where have you been?"

"Mahmoud! Oh my God! I forgot all about the meat!" She hurried along the bend in the alley and made for the street. The closer she got to the butcher's shop, the more anxious she became. She could hear her heart pounding. Her cheeks were hot and drops of sweat made their way down the curves of her face.

Mahmoud, the butcher's son, was standing on the sidewalk, closing the shop. The girl froze momentarily, then walked towards him. "Please don't close the shop yet. I need half a pound of meat for *abgusht.*" The boy threw a pointed, inquisitive look at the distressed girl and said

very gently "But we're out of meat, you're late." "But..."
She quickly turned her face away and started off. Mahmoud ran after her and touched Gharghad Goli's shoulder.
She felt a flame rising inside her. She did not know what
to do. She wished to remain there forever, feeling Mahmoud's hand on her shoulder. Instead, she quickly moved
away. "Why did you get upset? Come get the meat!"
Gharghad Goli did not respond. She just kept walking.
Since that day, Gharghad Goli had left the house everyday
and taken to the streets, and whether she needed meat or
not, she always passed the butcher's shop.

Her cousin came to see her one day and out of the blue,
asked her not to leave the house anymore. "People are
talking about you. They say you're acting wild, that you
make yourself up and walk all over the place." Even Rostam, her cousin, started giving her advice. He had
promised to come to her house and teach her how to read
and write, but one day he stopped by to tell her that some
ignorant people were talking a lot of nonsense behind her
back. The girl decided not to leave her house anymore
unless she had a reason, but she could not abide by her
own decision. The house was oppressive and an inner
desire directed her to the outside world again. Mahmoud
was very kind to her. She was falling in love unknowingly.
Every time she went to see him she wore her rose scarf.
Everyone knew her secret.

One evening, when she was at home with her parents,
her aunt came to visit. She was younger than her mother
but had five children and the youngest one, who was
Gharghad Goli's age was her friend. Her aunt's family
always came to visit all together, but this time she came by
herself. It was very unusual. When the girl brought them
tea, she noticed that her parents looked sad. She asked
"What's wrong, Aunt? Has something happened?" Her
aunt answered coldly "No, it's nothing". Well, something
was not right. Her aunt had come alone and everyone was
sitting there looking worried. Her mother said "Go sprinkle some water in the yard. It's all covered with dust." The

girl understood that she must leave them alone. She got up slowly and went to the yard. She took the hose, turned the faucet on and stared at the old tree.

Gharghad Goli's mother turned her gaunt face towards her husband and said "What are we going to do now? How can we hold our heads high after this scandal? Instead of helping us, the foolish girl has ruined our reputation." Her husband said, "But these could be all lies. People talk a lot. I don't think she is that sort of girl." Her aunt responded without hesitation, "There is something to what they say. I've seen her in front of the butcher's shop a couple of times myself. People don't just make up things. You didn't pay enough attention to her, didn't watch her closely. Pardon me for being nosy, but it isn't right. And her mother said "Sister, how could we help it? We're in the field all day long and there's no one else. What are we supposed to do?" Then the three of them were silent. The mother was melting inside, shaking her head from time to time. The father had a bitter smile on his face, making him look even more miserable. The aunt, who looked more relaxed now, was also thinking. They all mulled over the problem. The girl was accused of serious misconduct. She was no longer the same innocent, chaste girl she used to be. The mother blamed the butcher's son, murmuring that he was a Moslem and shouldn't have messed with their daughter, damaging their reputation like this. Finally the aunt broke her silence. "The only solution is to marry her off." Her father said "But how? We can't go soliciting for her!" Her mother said "Besides, with all these rumours going around, who's going to marry her? God, please help us!" The aunt tried to console her sister and told them that they must start looking, that they would be sure to find someone to marry her.

Gharghad Goli became restless outside. She cleaned the yard meticulously. Then she just stood there motionless. Finally she decided to go in. "We haven't had a visitor in so long, and now that we have one, they isolate me." She told her mother, while keeping her head down, "I've finished." She didn't hear an answer. She sat down while everyone ignored her. By now she was scared. What had happened? Why didn't they speak to her? Her mother's dull eyes were full of tears and her father's bent back looked even more crooked.

She didn't know why, but she somehow knew that she was responsible for their grief. Her aunt was not acting like the kind of woman she usually was, and looked at her grudgingly. She couldn't bear their silence any longer, so she said "What's the matter here?" But before she could find her voice, her aunt got up and left. Gharghad Goli had no idea what could be wrong. Her aunt bade her goodbye, looking as parched and unfeeling as desert sand.

They did not speak to her. Speaking wouldn't do them any good now. They felt they didn't know their daughter anymore. For the past year or so, the sense of family unity had been lost. No one had much to say. When evening came, they all went their own way, absorbed in their own thoughts. The distance between the parents and their daughter now seemed as long as their walk from their home to the field. The girl became anxious and sensed a disaster approaching. She didn't know what it was or why it had to happen but an intense anxiety had taken over her being and she awaited a catastrophe. She avoided every-one and kept her silence, but leaving the house was still the only thing that soothed her, and more than any other place, she found herself near the butcher's shop. She wouldn't even look up to see the butcher's son but know-ing that he was watching her made her heart jump. She did not delude herself. She knew she had no right to marry a Moslem man, yet she couldn't hold back her feet or stop the desperate beat of her heart. She continued wearing her rose scarf even though it was no longer new. Wearing it somehow made her eyes shinier.

That day her mother came back earlier than usual. She looked older, more fatigued and more resigned. The girl became anxious. Her mother started cleaning the house silently. Then she told her daughter to wear something decent. The girl was startled. She gathered that a guest was expected but she couldn't understand why her mother acted so reserved or why she didn't tell her who the guest was. She could do nothing but wait. She put on a clean dress and shrank into a corner. Her father came home. Having found more strength because of her husband's presence, her mother came to her and said "Today you should act properly because your future depends on it. Try to be nice but keep your head down. They're coming to ask for your hand. It's time you got married." The red on the girl's cheeks extended to her heart. She could not describe her feelings but she knew she was excited. She viewed this as a blessed opportunity; maybe her luck had struck. For a second she pictured the butcher's son in front of her and her heart sank deep down. It can't be... She pushed the thought back. Such a thing would be impossible. She could not think of anyone she knew among the Zoroastrians though. She asked her mother "Tell me who it is, mother. Please tell me before he comes." Overcoming a lump in her throat, her mother said "It's not important, my daughter. You have to accept whatever your fate has in store for you. We're not the ones who decide these things." Gharghad Goli needed to talk more but her mother rose and moved to the kitchen, leaving her stupified daughter alone.

There was a knock at the door. The father approached the door with feeble, reluctant steps. The girl was standing in a corner in the kitchen while her mother arranged a beautiful white scarf on her daughter's head. As the sound of the guests entering the house reached Gharghad Goli's mother, her hands froze on her daughter's shoulders, her eyes fixed on her daughter's. She was as still as a rock as if the exhaustion of years of hard work had taken the last mite of her energy. The girl surrendered, realising incredulously that it would be futile to resist. A remote hope replaced her fear, the hope of leaving her present state behind and putting an end to her neighbour's gossiping. She resigned herself to the old in the hope of the new. Suddenly she heard a familiar voice. She was so confused that she asked in an innocent, naive tone "What? What's that crazy Jamshid doing here?" Her mother's look was resigned and guilty. "My sweet daughter, everyone's fate..."

Gharghad Goli cried for a few days. They had decided to marry her off to Jamshid and be done with it. It was a cruel decision. It would ruin her life. Jamshid was retarded. Now they wanted her to spend the rest of her life with him. She could not accept this cursed fate. And her parents would not pay any attention to her objections. They were thinking only of their reputation, their honour, and how this man could help them win back what they had lost. Her father had shrunk even more and her mother's face was lined with new wrinkles. But they had made up their minds and perhaps they had no other choice. The girl could only cry.

Now Gharghad Goli had shrunk back in a corner and was sewing; she looked pathetic. Her eyes had sunk deep in their sockets and her face had lost its freshness. She heard a noise. Someone had come to visit. She kept on sewing, motionless, as the noise got louder and closer. It was her cousin Rostam who was making all this noise. He greeted her parents warmly, then he noticed Gharghad Goli, a frown developing on his face. He came near her and kindly asked her how she was. The girl threw her shoulders up coldly. Rostam sat down and said "Things have worked out beautifully for me. I have some free time now. I've come to start those lessons with your daughter, that is, if you don't mind." The father said "Dear Rostam! What good will lessons do her?" Rostam said "Dear uncle! When are you going to realise what's going on around you? Nowadays, every day is brimming with new events. After the riots two years ago, people are waking up. In the village where uncle Cyrus lives, people have thrown the big landowner out and divided the land. I hear they are much better off. Now it's our turn to show them we can do it too." The father said "Rostam. Settle down boy. I don't believe any of it. Besides, what does that have to do with

94

my girl learning her letters?" Rostam retorted "Then she can read the paper and tell you what's going on in the world!" The girl saddened by his idle enthusiasm, answered with a trembling voice "No, I can't learn now because I'm getting married." Her fury had found an outlet. She ran to the yard so she could cry by her loyal companion, the old tree. She could not hear their conversation anymore but she sensed an argument developing. She knew that Rostam was arguing against the marriage. But her father's loud voice cut short any hope. His agitated, feeble voice bleated out angry and unkind words. "Go away. Don't take sides with her!" Losing Rostam was going to be costly to them. He had been a loyal friend, someone who cheered them when they most needed it. Rostam's departure was the end of a phase in their solitary lives.

At dawn the girl shook her lean body and got up. She got dressed quietly, packed a bundle and went to the yard. She stood in front of the old cypress tree for a few minutes. Then she calmly looked at her parents. Tears formed in her eyes, making them glitter. She pulled her hair back and walked towards the door. All of a sudden a smile broke on her face. She quickly returned to the house and got her worn-out rose scarf. She arranged it on her head in front of the mirror, a proud lump forming in her throat. She approached the door again. She stopped to look at everything once more, then she opened the door and shut it behind her, knowing that she was leaving that house and her parents for good. The hot early morning breeze penetrated the scarf and lifted strands of her hair. Slowly something hardened in her eyes; a new resolve settled in, preparing for a long stay.

First published in Stories by Iranian Women Since the Revolution. *Reprinted with permission)*

Can You Hear Me?
by Amina Axmed Yuusuf (Somalia)

Can you hear me? Can I be heard?
As you poke me, dear doctor, with your long
Sharp finger, can you hear my cry of pain?
Can you hear me, soldier,
As you kill my mother and rape my sister and burn our village?
Can you hear me, my dear city,
For I can hear your cry as your heart is ripped out of its inner frame
And as your big walls are brought down,
Exposing you nakedly under the harsh African sky!
For I am dying and I am scared.
My short life has not come to mean much on a large world scale,
For I am no scholar or hero.
I have not climbed any great mountain or won any gold medal.
All I ever achieved is how to say "mother" at the age of two,
And how to sing at three;
At four I could dance and at five I learned how to die!

Can You Hear Me World?
You, world, who has come to this land of my forefathers
With your cameras, heavy military boots and guns.
World, my voice is weak, so I can no longer sing.
My legs are weak, so I can no longer dance,
And my arms are weak so I can no longer clap.
World, I have no hope of seeing a fairground or a zoo,
Of chasing rainbows or jumping through puddles.
For no one can hear me, so no one can see me.
I will sit in this room with all these other silent voices of death,
And I will wait until tomorrow, when I may no longer be

scared.
For then I will finally be free to fly through the heavens
and once again sing, dance and laugh.
I will sink into the deep embrace of my mother,
Who will comfort me so that I will never be scared again!

Daughter of The Desert
by Antonio Joaquim Marques (Angola)

Oh daughter of the desert
I am the last bird of thunder
Rider of storms in paths of wind
Tonight I bring you the water font of desire
In my tilting eyes of pleasurable love
Feel this my passionate pulse
I have come to plant hope in your suffering heart
In these vast scapes of your sand
And I shall trap the scorpions of death
And transform this land of fire dust
Into life and joy and serenity of oasis
Look how I plunge between the hemispheres
Through the night expanse of longing
I have come to make of your dry lips
The wet reflection of moonlight
Here then are my flowers of freedom
And my first calabash of rain
I weaved from the distant clouds
To quench your thirst of a thousand years
Now wipe away your tears my love
And dance with me to the restless winds
With harmony of dreams in the dark
I shall pluck the fingerless cactus
Sacred to the menstrual seasons
And when tomorrow comes
Peace shall descend upon this land
With my plumage of soothing breeze

Memories

Four Horses and a Wadi
by Abdirahman Mirreh (Somalia)

The G'u-rain arrived the drops
were not heavy the air was cold
the breeze light yet my hair
on my arms rose.

And slowly the wadi flowed;
no logs were floating;
no froth it carried.
Four horses grazed on its bank
testing the velocity with their
lips; aye! Fear.

How should they know
it unusually flow.

Dawn is Imminent
by Fawzi Karim (Iraq)

Pastures are bedewed this Sunday
I will drink straight from the bottle
A piece of cheese is enough
enough a spark in your pipe
to keep you warm

No café this Sunday
I will drink out of the bottle
till my shirt dampens
while the dawn spreads
Frightened by my footsteps will be
the squirrel
Through the mists of dawn — a door opens
I enter "Who are you?"
the doorman asks
"I am he who writes in metaphysical verse" I reply.

Thereupon, the dewy leaves are swept
aound me.
This Sunday, I deserted the house
crossing the crucial boundaries
between dreams and awareness
I deserted the house
crossing paths to reach a myth
no one else has crossed but me.

I drink out of the bottle
my hands fatigued
resisting a desire to roam in the pastures
for dawn is imminent
Through the mists of dawn — a door opens
I enter "Who are you?" the doorman asks
"I am he who writes metaphysical verse" I reply.

Like a cotton fountain
embittered, muffled silence,
My feet so flickering
vanish almost in my footsteps.
Waves of water
Propellers of palm on the banks
How to answer your call?

I will drink out of the bottle
till my breath smells bloodied
and spirit is cured
from the flesh.
I will toast to this ill-fated land
vanishing from the sight of days a house in Karch.

A friend melting in a pool of acid.
Another, like a scare-crow shepherds
the mine fields
What splinters and skulls
shanks
the mire giving them a dense presence
Sight of abating spirit
endless
Is this the resurrection of the lame or
is dawn imminent?

A piece of cheese is enough
enough a spark in your pipe
to keep you warm
No café this Sunday
I shall return home
and listen to the radio.

Lament
by Dara Sekulic (Bosnia)

To give birth meant nothing to us
My younger brothers, I do not remember all their names.
You were like earth
Perhaps that's why your lap was so warm.
Every autumn your white peasant skirt
Reddened from giving birth.

What colour was your hair?
The black kerchief reminded me of bread.
You decanted all springs on your back
If I knew where you lie buried,
I'd drive the earth to tears.

(Translated by Mario Susko)

(Permission to reprint kindly granted by Klaonica)

Kin The Beautiful

by Mabiala Molu (Zaire)

O Kin! Beautiful town so coveted
For you, Blacks and Whites made war,
Both claimed their right to fortune
And you, Ebony Princess, cast your spell on them.
Who did not succumb to your charms?
Who did not sing your praises?
For your love
Kallé became great,
Manu played the Cha-Cha
Senghor stopped at Léo
Césaire made himself loved
Fanon lived out his destiny
From the Maison Mère to the Congo Bar
They danced the Independence Cha-Cha
Kin the bold
Who can forget Dendhal with its maze of streets?
Who can forget the little "Mbongo and the Bills"?
Your lively lanes
Where women and girls bustled about
Gaily singing with their breasts in air
Your beloved roads
Where the men swaggered past
Your enchanting roads
Where Mbéleketé was shown off skillfully
Your sunny roads
Where the street musicians strolled up and down
Your beautiful avenues
Where the other people grew rich
And Angualima defied them
Your roads where once
Negro men and women danced the bamboula
And now, misery plays its game of fate
Kin MALEBO, Kin the promise
Town of leaders, town of light

Kin the beautiful, become the playground for miracles
Great city, devastated by those cockroaches
Jewel of an epoch, destroyed by those ruffians
O Beautiful Widow, cry for your heroes.

(Translated by Jennifer Langer)

Notes:

Kin = Kinshasa, capital of Zaire.
Whites = in the French, Toubabs is used. This is a term used for Whites by Africans.
Kalle = a popular singer.
Senghor = one of the founders of the Negritude movement, writing that draws heavily on the African past and identity rather than the colonial European tradition.
Léo = Leopoldville, the former name of the capital.
Manu Dibanga = Cameroonian musician.
Césaire = another founder of the Négritude movement, originally from Martinique.
Independence Cha-Cha = dance at the time of independence
Dendhal = area of Kinshasa with bars, clubs etc.
Mbélékete = a dance.
Angualima = a famous burglar who was never caught.
Malebo = port area of Kinshasa.
the tombola = lottery; many people were duped into selling property in the belief that they were certain to win. Many people lost everything.
playground for miracles = life is so difficult and miserable that the inhabitants hope for miracles to make their lives bearable.
Fanon = an Algerian writer who was involved in the anti-French colonial movement in the 60s.

Ma Terre d'O — My Land of O
by Muepu Muamba (Zaire)

No
Not only a trigger at the ready on the gun Africa my undu-
lating country I come from the land of fruity water-laden
like a pleasant orchard and in my heart surges dream
upon dream endlessly the hope of regaining my forfeited
country.

Zaire was once the realm of singing trees and shimmering
dreamy waters my land of O like a twin fairyland crescent
of tenderness the laughter burst forth corollas of flowers
like a bohemian seduction of pleasure

but
today my destitute likuta land is enthralled by misery how
can I tell you of the enchanting metamorphoses of my
ancient proud land when tears and mourning constantly
cast deadly shadows onto its azure bed

this
landscape of sweetness one day I may speak of the divine
bewitchment of munkamba and of kivu's proud gaze my
watery land of reflecting rivers softly caressing my watery
land an infinity of joyful rivers and smooth streams.

the
springs of airborne melodies are not exhausted yet so I
cannot really belong elewhere I who so long have lived
elsewhere my land of O.

(Translated by Denise Ganderton)

A Walk in the Valley
by Antonio Joaquim Marques (Angola)

As we walked
The yellow sun accompanied us
With its shy torch of smudge fires
Now hidden low in the ferns
Below where the warmth of new growth
Blossoms with gentle breeze
Over the sway of long hedgerows
Stretching to the meadow lakes
In vast emulation of a dream
That wore open larkspurs of pink
And a serene valley of sawgrass

So we talked to the dream
And the butterflies swung their wings
Through the wide voyage upstream
With gestation of eggs
For the new pupation of life
All was well and tranquil here
And we wished it was peace every day
As purple shells on marshes of wild weeds
Made slow circles like songs creeping
Within and beyond a bending walkway
On rafters of waves with harmony

All was well when suddenly
An island of terror surrounded us
The mythic hawk of the savannah
Rehearsed a hollow chorus of havoc
Of too many seasons of destruction
And a broken grave near the lonely grove
Exposed its castaway corpse to remind us
The horror phantom glee from the sockets
Of he who just died by a stray bullet
In the skull.

Whine

by Dubravka Ugresic (Bosnia)

Sometimes I wonder whether what drove me out of my country was, in fact, music. That is, the reasons for going into exile are often far less serious than one imagines. After all, if someone can go mad because of their sensitivity to sounds, I don't see why a similar kind of sensitivity (a sense of taste for instance), could not be the reason for someone to leave their homeland. Be that as it may, every exile often feels that the state of exile is a special kind of sensitivity to sound; sometimes I feel that exile is nothing but a state of unconscious musical recollection (which may be agreeable or disagreeable).

One day I went into the centre of Munich to meet my acquaintance Igor, but some way from Marienplatz I stopped, drawn to the sound of music. An elderly gypsy was playing Hungarian gypsy songs on a violin. He caught my passing glance, gave me a smile that was at the same time deferential and brazen, recognising me as one of his kind. Something caught in my throat, for a moment I couldn't breathe, and then I lowered my eyes and hurried on, realising a second later that I had set off in the wrong direction. A couple of paces further on I caught sight of a life-saving telephone box and joined the queue, pretending that I had to make a phone call, what else. There was a young man standing in front of me, tight black leather jacket, tight jeans, high-heeled boots, a kind of insecurity and impudence on his face at the same time, like colours running into each other. A second later, I knew that he was one of "us", my countryman. The way he slowly and persistently dialled the number — looking neither to right nor left, like a waiter in a cheap restaurant — filled me with a mixture of anger and pity and put me on the side of the people in the queue. And then the young man finally got through (yes, one of us, of course!). My countryman's habit of talking for a long time about nothing, as if coddling, pampering, mutually patting each other's backs and jollying each other along, that habit filled me again with a sudden mixture of anger and pity. The violin was still whining sorrowfully, the young man was talking to a certain Milica, and in my head, as at an editing table, I was joining the whine to the young man's babbling. The black-eyed violinist was staring persistently in my direction. For a moment I wanted to leave the queue, but I didn't, that would have given me away, I thought. That is why, when the young man finished his conversation and smoothed his hair with his hand, (a gesture which filled me with the same mixed feelings as before, because of its unexpectedness), I telephoned Hannelore, who was the only person I could have telephoned, thinking up some urgent, practical question.

I was late for my meeting with Igor. We went to a Chinese restaurant and as we chatted while waiting to be served, I observed that I was restless, absent, that my eyes were wandering. I felt as though I was covered with a fine film, like spectacles on a winter's day. At one moment I was conscious of a sound which I had not registered at first. There was pop music playing, Chinese or Korean, or at any rate, pop music from some eastern part of the world. It was a soft, elegiac, sweet crooning, a love song presumably, which could have been from my home or from Igor's Russian home. Just then there was a sudden downpour of rain which streamed down the restaurant window, behind Igor, and finally I broke down, let myself go, reacted properly, exactly, according to an ancient, well-practised reflex, of which I had not been conscious until that moment. In a word, I salivated at the sound of the bell, that universal, sweet whine, the same whine no matter where it came from. I struggled inwardly, resisted, grumbled, almost glad that I was in its power, almost physically satisfied. Quite softened, I splashed about in the warm invisible puddle of tears... "What's happening, Igor..?" I asked him as though apologising. "I understand," he replied. "I myself belong to a provincial, tango culture," explained my friend, a Russian Jew from Chernovitsa, an exile.

(Permission to reprint kindly granted by Erewhon)

Land

by Sherko Bekas (Kurdistan)

When I touched the bough of a tree
It trembled in pain
When I held out my hand to the branch
the trunk started to weep
when I embraced the trunk
the soil under my feet shuddered
the rocks groaned

this time when I bent down and collected
a handful of earth
all Kurdistan screamed.

Through the Vast Halls of Memory 2
by Haifa Zangana (Iraq)

Zino is the brightness of light and its crystallisation; the many colours of the mountains, the red mountains with their black summits. The colours seem to be unlimited. The huge caves invite you to leave the mountain trail, to enter and discover the cool darkness, dripping water, the scent of moss and the hanging plants. Routine has its own richness. Tobacco fields and pellucid views. It is a refuge, a conscious longing for the mother's womb and father's lap. Snow and mountain top; snow sold by children during summer. The rugged mountain tracks. Nature radiant as if behind glass; springs are crystallised moon and snow. Pomegranates and vines. The moment of meeting a shepherd and his goats on their way home of an evening; the blue water washing the coloured rocks, the beautiful faces of the women and their colourful dresses. What sadness had those women felt when they were forced to leave their homes and live in tents in another country?

Zino was just a long, muddy road surrounded by houses built of rock brought from the mountains nearby. In the village there were a number of alleys starting at the muddy road and ending at the foot of the rugged mountains. The main road in the village was narrow, not because of any error in the original plan, but owing to the shopkeepers' persistence in displaying half of their wares on the road. Thus, sacks of rice, wheat and barley, sat besides children's clothes, rubber shoes, fabrics, sewing needles and cotton together with heaps of old magazines, religious and Marxist tracts in Arabic, Persian and Turkish, with a few publications in Kurdish. In small wooden boxes were knives, forks, spoons and kitchen utensils. Next to these were all kinds of pills, including pain-killers and pills to combat indigestion. And, believing Zino to be one of the most popular resorts, visited by thousands of tourists daily, the shopkeepers insisted on exhibiting postcards and local handicrafts. Each day at 5pm, the shop-keepers hauled their goods back into their shops, to re-exhibit them the next morning. Zino women are always in a hurry. On their shoulders falls the responsibility of look-ing after husbands and children and taking care of sewing tapestry and weaving. Bedspreads have to be ready for winter, so little pieces of material are carefully collected and arranged in beautiful patterns to make sheets and bedspreads for young brides. Women also have to gather wood from the mountains, load it on the backs of their mules (or their own backs, if they have no mules), help their husbands at farming and in building temporary sum-mer huts from leaves and branches in the hope of letting them to tourists.

I was eight years old when my father took me with him Zino. He was proud to see me reading and writing Arabic, to the extent that he forgot to teach me his mothertongue. Although he was fluent in Kurdish, Persian and Assyrian, Arabic remained a closed book to him.

We arrived in the village at noon. The road was empty and the shops open, with half their contents outside on the street. It was the time for prayer, lunch and siesta. We headed for a half-built house, passing an incomplete fence, and went through a room with no door or window. As we reached the wooden door, Mam Mahmoud opened it, wel-coming and hugging my father and me in turn. The room was almost empty except for a huge wooden box in one cor-ner. On it there were blankets, cotton covers and round pillows. From the other corner, there came the smell of tea brewing in a samovar, and the scent of burning coal. I was fascinated by a beautiful, multi-coloured Persian rug which added its warm, welcoming atmosphere to the room.

A few minutes later Mam Mahmoud's wife walked in, carrying a tray with four tea cups. She put it beside the samovar and shook hands with my father and then hugged me. As I could understand very little of what they were saying in Kurdish, I occupied myself in watching the cubes of sugar as they dissolved in the tea, which I stirred continuously, making enough noise to attract the adults' attention. I expected my father to be angry, as he would have been at home. Instead, he remained silent and relaxed, sipping his tea as if time had lost its importance.

In that room, my father's presence was different from in the city. He questioned Mam Mahmoud about relatives and what they were doing and he talked about the city. Mam Mahmoud talked about problems with the border guards and how times had changed. Mam Jin was silent most of the time and when she spoke , she asked my father to make an appointment with a gynaecologist. Mam Mahmoud said nothing until he commented that the time was getting late... I whispered, "Why can't we stay in Zino?" In the way he sat and in his green eyes, I could see the meaning in his coming back to a place where he could stretch out and touch familiar things and feel that oblivion could not reach him.

And I felt the urge to touch him, to make sure it really was him, the man who was lost to us in the big city. He sensed my feeling and stroked my hair tenderly. I whispered, "Why can't we stay here?" He did not reply. The city was his dream, being married to an Arab woman was his dream, and being proud of a daughter excelling in her studies and politics was also his dream. "The cold weather has arrived early this year," was a phrase of Mam Mahmoud's as he quietly stepped out, on the outlook for the last birds of summer. He walked ahead of us, towards one of the shops, which unlike the rest, was locked up. He unlocked the door and, from the darkness within, came an unforgettable smell. In the years that followed, and in moments of despair, that smell turned out to be the only window open on the sky: the smell of darkness, humidity and mounds of Persian carpets rolled up in a certain way to keep them safe from moths. I jumped on them and as my father gave instructions, I helped Mam Mahmoud pull one out. Mam Mahmoud unrolled the carpet in front of the shop. How beautiful it was! Fascinated, I stood there gazing at the endless patterns and bright colours. Moving closer, I felt the woolly texture, trying to imitate and upstage my father in savouring its smell. Mam Mahmoud laughed and hugged me again. That day we bought two carpets. Then we started our journey back to the city.

Homesickness
by Mohammed Khaki (Kurdistan)

If one day
your jasmine sweet memory
came with the zephyrs of spring
ruffling the pages of my poetry —
Which drop of rain
would wash away my homesickness

My Wish
by Mohammed Khaki (Kurdistan)

In my dreams
I come to your tent
filling my shepherd's basket with
the songs of mountain starlings.
I am making a bed of sweet violets
entwining my arms as honeysuckle
for you.

On The Way to Mecca
by Hushang Mehr-Ayin (Iran)

That something was odd about Dr Mobini there is no question. But to blame him for all our troubles in that long, hot summer of 1325 (1946 AD) would be wrong. The people in the neighbourhood finally managed to force him out of his house in the alley, but they continued to experience troubles even worse than those they went through in that summer.

Dr Mobini was the owner of the modern Markazi Pharmacy on Pahlavi Avenue close to Kutche Bidi. The pharmacy closed down soon after he left our neighbourhood. He had moved into one of the six houses in our alley belonging to Mr Afshar.

In the beginning, the people in the neighbourhood were happy to see a well-to-do family moving in. Dr Mobini was, after all, the owner of one of the famous pharmaceutical shops in the city. He had the house properly repaired and redecorated before moving in. Haj Nasrollah, one of the elders of our small community, made discreet enquiries about the new neighbour and was quite happy to learn that he was a quiet and respectable doctor. He was looking forward to giving him a warm and hearty welcome on behalf of the neighbours.

Unfortunately, from that point, things began to go wrong. Dr Mobini proved to be too quiet for Haj Nasrollah's liking. He seemed at first not to respond to Haj Nasrollah's attempts to make him feel welcome and at home in the neighbourhood. Nobody knew exactly what had happened between Haj Nasrollah and Dr Mobini. What was known was Haj Nasrollah's version of the event. He said he had tried hard to catch Dr Mobini either leaving or entering his house so as to make his acquaintance. But he had failed — it seemed to him that Dr Mobini was like a ghost, leaving his house and then entering it in the evenings without anybody noticing him.

One Friday morning Haj Nasrollah actually knocked at Dr Mobini's door, which was opened after a long wait. Dr Mobini opened the door wide enough to stick his bald head out without allowing Haj Nasrollah to glance inside the courtyard. He was not unduly rude to Haj Nasrollah, but he was not polite either. He did not invite Haj Nasrollah in, nor did he engage in any kind of neighbourly conversation. His mannner was such that Haj Nasrollah quite forgot what he wanted to say; he simply said that as a neighbour he was welcoming Dr Mobini to the neighbourhood and was ready to extend any help which the doctor or his family might need. The doctor thanked him perfunctorily and after saying there was no need for the neighbours to worry about him, had quickly closed the door.

There and then Haj Nasrollah decided that something was inexplicably off about the new neighbour. Nor did he hesitate to let everybody in the neighbourhood think that there was indeed something suspicious about Dr Mobini. Not everybody in the neighbourhood would have agreed with Haj Nasrollah so easily when it came to judging other people's character. After all, Haj Nasrollah was the owner of the two biggest grocery stores in the locality and was known to overcharge his customers. "I'm sure there is something odd about him," said Haj Nasrollah to some of his neighbours on a Thursday afternoon at the customary monthly Rouzeh-Khani in his house. "What do you think is wrong with him?" asked Mr Karamat, the real estate dealer who lived in the alley in a house in which two rooms were let to Hashem Agha, the husband of Batool Khanum. "That is what I don't know," replied Haj Nasrollah. "I know something must be wrong with him, but I'm not sure what. That's what I'm going to find out. His presence in our locality might bring us bad luck. Such matters must not be taken lightly. After all, what do we know about the Dr Mobini?" Mr Feizi, an employee of the Ministry of Finance, who lived next door to Haj Nasrollah, suggested the best thing was to leave Dr Mobini alone. He said people in the neighbourhood must be glad to see a quiet and seemingly respectable person living in a house which only two or three months ago had been inhabited by two large families with ten noisy children. "Let's be thankful to God that all those noisy people have gone and that their place has been taken by respectable people like Dr Mobini," Mr Feizi said. Mr Feizi was a sensible man and his remarks reflected public opinion in the neighbourhood. In fact, for two years, Mr Karamat and several other neighbours had written petitions to the local branch of the municipality complaining that conditions in the houses owned by Mr Afshar were below the accepted standard and that either Mr Afshar must be forced to repair the houses or the municipality must demolish them. And for more than two years, all the residents in the alley had been fed up with the noise and the other inconvenience caused by the tenants of Mr Afshar. It was eventually Mr Feizi who used his influence as a middle-ranking employee of the Ministry of Finance to frighten Mr Afshar into evicting his tenants and putting his houses up for sale. During all these years Haj Nasrollah, who always regarded himself as the elder of the community, did not raise a finger to help people. And now that finally Mr Afshar's houses had been evacuated and one of them rebuilt for Dr Mobini to occupy, some individuals like Haj Nasrollah, were coming forward to create unnecessary problems.

People in the neighbourhood were apparently destined to mount a hate campaign and Dr Mobini was to be its target. Unfortunately, at that time a succession of disasters hit the neighbourhood which intensified the hate campaign and made Dr Mobini an unavoidably good target.

Firstly, there was the sudden illness of Batool Khanum's infant son which the doctors could not cure. Subsequently the neighbours decided that the infant was the victim of an evil eye cast on him by Dr Mobini. Secondly, there was the collapse of the roof in one of Mr Afshar's empty and dilapidated houses. At the time of the collapse two boys were playing in the house and were trapped under the debris. They had to be rescued and

117

rushed to hospital. Thirdly, Mr Karamat was involved in an accident which could have cost him his life. He fell from the balcony of a three-storey house as he was showing it to would-be buyers. He broke some bones but was eventually saved and cured. Fourthly, there was the unexpected release of Hashem Agha from prison. It wa learned afterwards that Mr Feizi was instrumental in getting him released, but at the time everybody assumed that Dr Mobini's evil spirit got him out of prison so that he might return to the neighbourhood to cause trouble. Hashem Agha was apparently told while in prison that Haj Nasrollah was secretly arranging with Mr Karamat to get a divorce for Batool so he could marry her. So when he got out of prison he made an unsuccessful and clumsy attempt on Haj Nasrollah's life. Finally there were the rainstorms in the middle of summer which caused floods in Teheran and, as far as our neighbourhood was concerned, completely ruined Mr Afshar's houses.

At this juncture, I should say that the residents of the alley were not a bunch of superstitious, illiterate and backward individuals. Two families in the locality owned private cars, and there was a radio set in almost every house. Although most of the families were migrants from the provinces, they were all relatively prosperous and of high standing. Except for Haj Nasrollah's wife and a couple of old women, there was no chadouri woman in the locality. Even Haj Nasrollah's two girls did not wear the chadour; one of them was about to finish secondary school. Some women, such as Batool Khanum and Mr Karamat's wife, used to wear the chadour, not because they were religious but merely for convenience. Even so, they would wear modern dress whenever they went to visit relatives, neighbours or friends. The people in our area were considered modern by the standards of Teheran at that time, towards the second half of the twentieth century.

The community was already tense when the first of the disasters struck — the sudden illness of Batool's infant son. Batool was a beautiful and shapely young woman, married to Hashem Agha who owned part of a transport firm on Sepah Avenue. Hashem Agha was forced to move from Kermanshah to Teheran because of his business. And in Teheran he chose to live in two rooms in Mr Karamat's house because Mr Karamat was a relative of Batool. And Mr Karamat, an experienced real estate agent, was looking around to buy a suitable house for Hashem. Unfortunatly Hashem was involved in a traffic accident and put in jail. Though Mr Karamat promptly assumed guardianship over Batool and her son, it was obvious she would behave as she desired. She had plenty of money and could afford to dress well and go out on shopping sprees to Lalehzar and Naderi. Nobody suggested she was wayward; but her beauty and immaculate appearance would obviously attract other men to her and the fact that her husband was away could have encouraged some men to make undue advances to her. Moreover, she used to breast-feed her baby sitting on a stool in front of the house talking and chatting with neighbours. Every man in the neighbourhood had cast his eyes on Batool's shapely breasts as she fed her son. And then she used to take her son to the doctors for the flimsiest of reasons.

So, when she said that her son was seriously ill, at first nobody believed her. But he was genuinely sick and the doctors could not cure the baby's high temperatures. Finally, on Mrs Karamat's suggestion, it was decided to seek a traditional cure. Mrs Karamat knew an old woman who had successfully cured similar cases. Later all the women assembled at Mrs Karamat's house to watch the old woman, Ma'soumeh Khanum, perform her magic. They all took an oath not to inform the authorities about the presence of Ma'soumeh Khanum and her magical treatment. According to eye-witnesses, Ma'soumeh Khanum was brought in a taxi and rushed into the house. Once those present, all women, were seated round the copper tray full of ash, she ordered a raw egg and a bowl of water to be brought in. She was to determine whether the baby had been struck by an evil eye. So the bowl of water was placed on the ashes in the tray. She placed an egg on top of the ashes, then she took a piece of charcoal in her hand and began to recite some strange and unintelligible words. The women were all silent, holding their breath as Ma'soumeh Khanum recited the verses. Once her recital ended, she began to call the names of the baby's relatives and other people who might have cast their eyes on him and as she called a name she gently touched the charcoals on the white shell of the egg. She called many names and nothing happened; finally, somebody suggested that she pronounced Dr Mobini's name. She did so, and before she had even touched the white shell of the egg with charcoal, the egg cracked on the ashes in the tray. It was an incredible sight; everybody present could see that nothing had touched the egg, and it was so quiet that the water in the bowl remained still. Yet, the shell of the egg cracked as Ma'soumeh Khanum called Dr Mobini's name. With the cracking of the egg, the ceremony was over and the culprit identified. Ma'soumeh Khanum took some wax in her hands and made an effigy of Dr Mobini. Then she pierced the eyes of the effigy with a pin while reciting some strange words. She was paid 50 tomans, an enormous sum in those days, and left quietly. Less than 24 hours later, the baby had duly recovered from his illness.

The incident left no doubt in the minds of the residents that Dr Mobini was indeed wicked and that he could cast an evil eye on people. Then they began to wonder why he had chosen our alley to settle down in. Gradually, agitation to force him out of our locality began. Haj Nasrollah and Mr Karamat would not be deterred; they assumed the mantle of leadership and organised a popular movement to evict Dr Mobini. And their hand was strengthened when the roof of the house next to Mr Karamat's collapsed. Luckily the boys trapped under the debris were rescued in time. In fact the house, which belonged to Mr Afshar, was in ruins and it was inevitable that the roof would one day fall in. But coming so soon after the egg-cracking incident, it was clear that people would blame Dr Mobini for it. The other incidents merely added fuel to an already explosive situation. Under normal conditions, nobody would have seen an evil hand in Mr Karamat's dangerous fall from a balcony or in Hashem Agha's anger at Haj Nasrollah. Of course, heavy rain in Teheran in the middle of summer could not be easily explained. So two days after the rain and the resulting floods, when people had managed to clean up the mess, an angry mob stormed Dr Mobini's house.

For nearly half an hour the mob waited as Haj Nasrollah knocked at the door demanding to see Mr Mobini. Curiously, there was no response. Somebody said it was too early for Dr Mobini to be at home and that he might be at his pharmacy. But Haj Nasrollah paid no attention to this sensible advice and continued to pound on the door demanding to see Dr Mobini. While the angry mob waited, somebody from among the crowd hurled three rocks at the windows of the house behind the wall, across the courtyard. The sound of breaking glass frightened the crowd, who backed away slightly. By this time two policemen had arrived, but they were not eager to intervene. Then Amir Khan came in a hurry and tried to talk Haj Nasrollah out of breaking into the house. Though very strong and a good wrestler, Amir Khan was too gentle to use force against Haj Nasrollah. He tried to restrain the Haji gently, but to no avail. Word was sent to Mr Feizi and he dispatched somebody by taxi to fetch Dr Mobini from the pharmacy. Good old Feizi even paid the taxi fare out of his own pocket. The crowd finally broke in before Dr Mobini could arrive. Luckily, Amir Khan was able to keep the mob away from the rooms. Using some force but relying on his powers of friendly persuasion, Amir Khan asked the mob to wait while he talked to the residents. It was then that the people in the neighbourhood learned the secret of Dr Mobini's household. When the mob was partly inside the courtyard and while Amir Khan was trying to keep them away from the rooms, a pale and frail-looking girl appeared at the door of the hall leading to the courtyard.

She was shaken and visibly shocked. Amir Khan approached her and said something which nobody heard. It was the first time the people had seen a member of Dr Mobini's family. Nobody knew what had passed between the girl and Amir Khan, but he ran back to the mob and began to shout abuse. No one had ever seen Amir Khan so angry or so impolite before. He grabbed Haj Nasrollah with his two hands and lifting him up, used him as a shield to push the crowd out of the courtyard into the alley. His one-man crusade forced the mob out of the house. By this time, Dr Mobini had arrived, accompanied by Mr Feizi and another neighbour called Mr Shoughi, who was believed to be a Bahai. Strange as it may seem, Dr Mobini was cool, composed and not shocked. He asked Mr Feizi, Mr Shoughi and Amir Khan to enter the house with him. The two policemen began to attend belatedly to their duties, dispersing the crowd. A little later, Mr Feizi's manservant, who had previously gone by taxi to fetch Dr Mobini, was seen running to Mr Hamidi's house. Mr Hamidi's was the only household in the locality with a telephone. From his house they called the hospital to send an ambulance to take Mrs Mobini to hospital.

Within a week, Dr Mobini had left our neighbourhood — the wish of the people had been fulfilled. Nobody knows where the family went. But more serious disasters hit the community. Before the arrival of winter, Haj Nasrollah too had left the neighbourhood and sold his grocery store, much to the delight of his business rival Mr Yazdani. By next summer, Mr Karamat was so seriously ill he had to sell his house and go to Damavand to retire.

Two years later, our blind alley was included in a re-development scheme and its shape was completely changed, And the so-called friendly neighbourhood community was no longer.

My Father's Dream
by Sargon Boulos (Iraq)

One night
my father saw a saint in his dream
He saw a tall saint
who spoke to him
with eyes burning like two embers
in a voice full of authority
very sure of being obeyed

In the morning
my father went out
to knock on village doors
one after another
to tell his dream
while he rolled a cigarette
of cheap tobacco
with the face of somebody
returned from war
or a soldier staring in amazement
at the stump of his amputated thigh

He had forgotten to shave for many days
and was jobless for as long as history
In his hands that knew
only how the hammer weeps
as it drives his days with cuneiform
tears into the heart of wood
in his hands of skin and bone
he stubbornly clutched the rosary
of the future with orphan beads
and saw winter
after winter
send the carriage of hope
rolling off into a snowstorm
to disappear, trailed by a star
and a pack of emaciated wolves

He kept knocking on the doors
one after another
the sack of burlap on his back
filling up as evening advanced
with loaves of bread, the village's
black rice, tea and salt
whenever he told his dream
which he did more than fifty times
till I knew it by heart

He had taken me along
to carry the sack when he got tired.

The Mare
by Fouad Mirza (Iraq)

He miraculously managed to flee and run with all his might, crossing mountains and deserts, plains and valleys, rivers and oceans. He appeared in front of us with a demeanour certain to make any sane person scream with fright.

He had escaped from death and miraculously slipped from hell. His eyes were prominent and protruding, his hair had taken on the colour of mud, tar and soot, his face reflected the undulations and rain and gales of the land he had crossed. He was out of breath. His mouth had become like a dried abyss, which muttered mysterious, disjointed words, that left only one impression, that this wretched young man was trembling with fear.

Me and my three friends occupied a little room, the darkest and dampest in the world. It was quite natural that we should make space for this quivering creature, a place on the floor for him to sleep on and to share our meals.

For many days we had concluded but not with any certainty, through guesswork from his fragmented speech, that this fugitive from the jaws of hell was called "Jawad." His personal documents, yellowed and tattered, with their lost and faded words, were of no help to us in unravelling any information other than that he was a native of Iraq.

We did not know for certain which part of Iraq he came from, whether it was from a village or a city, from the north or the south. But that did not bother us at all, for in him we saw our reflection, a true reflection with no retouching of our anxious consciences or souls exhausted by ghosts, the dead and our suspicions. Whenever we woke up in the darkness screaming from a nightmare, we would find him already awake before us, with his protruding eyes and muddied hair, sitting there jerky and

125

inspecting every corner on the verge of... Our nightmares occurred in slumber, but his nightmares accompanied him in his awakening, continously and forever. We used to tend, nurture, guard and nurse him just like a real brother.

Sometimes, occasionally, we found employment, any work, as we used to offer our services as a group for decorating, distributing leaflets, cleaning and such like. We would collect and save our earnings carefully, not giving a thought to luxuries and other trivialities, and in so doing we formed a real wretched family unit or literally a small community.

We once thought of taking Jawad with us, perhaps the working atmosphere might bring him back to his senses and make him forget his fears. However, before we reached the apartment building, the manager had obstructed us, standing in our way, hands on hips.

Six months had elapsed in the course of which Jawad stopped taking his meals regularly. He seemed more anxious than ever, silent and staring at the light. With his eyes and fingers he always signalled to the corners where weird creatures and invisible visions besieged him so that he started screaming. We used to smother his mouth with our hands, but he used to bite us and escape. One day we were surprised by the presence of the landlady, who was by all accounts, a dirty, rancid old woman, standing on the threshold, threatening to evict us if we began quarrelling again. We swore to her that there was no quarrel and that the cries that everyone heard were only that of our ill friend. But she renewed her threats with her fist, spitting on the floor, making a loathsome, chirping sound between her teeth... Arabs! We thought of taking him to a doctor, but since we did not have any medical insurance, we had to content ourselves with sedatives which we crushed and mixed with his tea and meals.

One evening, having left him earlier in the room with a tape recorder and Iraqi songs, we found the door open

126

on our return, the lock dismantled and Jawad absent. Jawad had fled and returned to the enemy!

I do not know whose idea it was, but it seemed that one of us had expected such an ending. We had written our address and placed it in a little leather purse on a chain round his neck, in the same way that bells are hung on thoroughbred horses. Since we did not have a telephone, we received a letter from an official source which contained the following:

"We found this address on a person of unknown identity. Will anyone who knows or is related to the deceased, kindly contact us at the following address." At the bottom of the page there was the address. The date was the previous week's. Jawad was dead. He had stopped running.

His invisible presence remained with us for many months after, with his mysterious shadow as he approached us, the rustling of his footsteps, his muted sounds in the rooms and his sudden, lonely cries, its echo reverberating for a long time before disappearing in the vacuum of silence.

After the post-mortem, Jawad was kept on ice for three days. The body was finally returned to us. The Iraqi Said* came to our aid and promised to take on the burial costs. In front of us, he washed and shrouded him, in the middle of a room on a long dining room table with chipped paint. He bathed the body, perfumed it with musk and rose water, placing between his teeth strange scented herbs. The cemetery was far and snow was beginning to fall. It was a large, cold cemetery, in fact a lonely forest, dense with giant pine trees. It was divided into sections. We penetrated deep amongst the crosses and Stars of David, until we reached the arid heights, where the exiled Muslims buried their dead. The Said said "A little dust... dust over the deceased is favourable." It was cold weather. Jawad was calm, clean and covered with the whiteness of his shroud, with only his Iraqi face showing.

A year after we had separated, we agreed to keep in touch so that if one of us died, the others would undertake his burial. Perhaps and like Jawad, when we are transformed to mere shadows, invisible, fearless shadows, we will return, only free this time.

***Said** = a Muslim religious figure

(Translated by Lily Al-Tai)

Beledweyn
by Maxamed Ibraahim 'Hadraawi' (Somalia)

*The poet accompanied a troupe of actors to Beledweyn, a
country town, where he met a girl for whom he composed
this mock-romantic poem.*

Love! May you live for evermore!
It can't be true — it's a lie, I say,
That it was you who killed Bowndheri!
Love! May you live for evermore!
It can't be true — it's a lie, I say,
That your piercing iron-hard thrust
To liver, heart and flank
Is a wound no physic can heal
Nor nursing mend — it can't be true!

When I went down to Beledweyn
The times were blest and prosperous.
The river had overtopped its banks
And bestowed its water on the farmlands,
Grass fit for grazing covered the ground
And trees and bushes were bedecked with blooms.
The maize and millet were threshed and winnowed
And the grapes were now all ripe.
There was a *bullo* dance, and others, too —
People danced and danced till dawn's first light
As the homesteads rejoiced in the season of spring.

Now, in that town, on the eastern side,
There lives a queen!
Resplendent she is as sun-gilt water,
And the beauty and charm of womanhood
Are found in her to true perfection.
Her long hair falls as far as her heels —
I could compare it only with ostrich plumes —
And on the crown of her head there are auburn shades

Which evenly sweep to right and left.
Her locks are anointed with scented ghee
And they serve her even when she sleeps
For does not her body rest on them?
Are they not a pillow for her head?
Does she not spread them as a coverlet?

And when I met her —
Ah, what a fervent longing,
What joy she planted in me!

It was in the morning, early,
On the eighth day of the month,
In Beledweyn, halfway across the Swaying Bridge
That spans the water, swinging to and fro —
It was there we chanced upon each other,
Beerlula and I.
I stopped and spoke to her in greeting
And she returned me words of welcome.
We arranged to meet — it was fate —
She said, "Be here tomorrow!"
Didn't she?

"I can't face the journey home —
I'm desperately ill —
Please cancel the departure —
Consider the state I'm in!"
But the news of my affliction was not welcomed —
"We're off today!" was the troupe's response.
The director even thought that I was lying —
That harsh and wicked man ignored my plight
And didn't want to know about it, did he?
Then most of the troupe got on the truck —
Quite blatantly they did it —
They all climbed up from one side
And I had to climb up from the other.

When strong feelings get out of hand
And longings overpower the mind,
One prays sometimes for evil things to happen
And did I refrain from this? I didn't, no!
I prayed that some part inside the truck,
Some metal part, would cease to work,
I prayed that the petrol-tank would spring a leak,
I even prayed that the driver would get ill
And not recover before departure time.

At dawn, and through the first hot morning hours
Far on the horizon we could see a giant shape,
The massive tree that all Beledweyn knows as Baar.
The wind rushed through its withered pods —
We heard it calling out to us —
We heard it whistling, didn't we?

The truck went rocking on its way,
Back and forth and side to side,
And grievous illness gripped me again.
The evening heat rose towards me from the dunes
And I fainted.
Beerlula seemed to be at my side
A green meadow lay beneath our feet
The season was prosperous, the times propitious,
And together we danced the *beerrey* dance —
But now my senses returned to me
And what had it been but a deluding dream?

Like a bird of prey on the wing
The truck sped on and on
And climbed to the top of a lofty hill.
As I gazed around me,
Peering now to one side, now on the other,
It came into my mind to jump —
I cared nothing for the risk of death!

I am a man who has been bewitched
I long to be not here, but there —
Not in Banaadir, where I'm living now,
But in Beledweyn — that is where I want to be!
I look for her, I call her name — Beerlula!

Oh God — make Beledweyn a garden of solace and joy!
Oh God — make Beledweyn an abode of happiness!
Oh God — turn aside from Beerlula any threatening harm!
Oh God — let her live in peaceful and prosperous times!

(Permission to reprint kindly granted by Sheila Andrzejewski)

Resistance

A Man and a Woman
by Antonio Cabral (Angola)

A man and woman lived in a village in Angola. They were a happy couple. However, the man was in the habit of going out at night to steal chickens, goats and pigs from other people's sheds and kraals.

One night he went out as usual. The whole village was sleeping. He went to a kraal and seized a goat. On his return home, his wife asked "Where did you get this from?" The man answered "A wife should not ask." The night passed. The following day they started consuming the goat, leaving only the bones. The man went out again another night. This time he brought back a pig. The pig was dead but there were no spots of blood. Again his wife asked "Where did you get this from?" Again the reply was "A wife should not ask." The woman did not utter a word.

In the meantime, the village people started complaining vociferously. "My goat has been stolen." "My pig has gone." Others swore and cursed saying "If the person does not own up, he will die a horrible death." Meanwhile in the couple's house, meat was abundant. While some hung on the rope to dry, the roasted meat lay in large, clay pots ready to eat.

Another day dawned. The woman thought and thought "I can't live a life like this." When the man went out, she ran to the pastor's house to report everything that was happening. "I can't stand it any more. I've had enough." The pastor asked the woman to tell him exactly what was happening. The pastor listened attentively and then told the woman to return home. "We shall talk about it next Sunday in church," he said. The woman

133

agreed and left the pastor's house and off she walked back home.

The days went by very fast. Then it was then Sunday in church. The church was as crowded as a swarm of ants. The pastor preached and the sermon was about theft. The listeners, moved by the subject, shook their heads and murmured "Stealing is evil and wrong." When the service ended, the people dispersed to their various homes.

Only a few days had passed when the woman's husband reverted to his previous habit of stealing and decided to go and target more distant villages. The man went out again at night. His wife thought deeply about the matter and again ran to the pastor's residence to tell him of the events. The pastor listened carefully and finally said: "I understand. Return home. I'll be there soon with a witness." The woman agreed and left. The pastor invited one of his congregants to accompany him. They put on their coats and off they went to investigate the matter. They hid among the bushes at the back of the house and waited for the man to return. Finally, when the cold was starting to bite, the pastor and the churchgoer heard some human footsteps. It was dawn and the cocks were crowing. The man arrived with his load. As he was about to step into the house, the two men were at the door "May we come in? What's going on here?" the pastor asked. The man was speechless. Then the pastor said "It's late. We'll talk in the morning. We'll be off now." They left.

In the morning as the sun rose, the couple moved out. They were nowhere to be seen and the marriage was over.

Note:
The above fable is an allegory representing the final, bitter separation between UNITA and the MPLA in 1992.

A Man and a Woman
by Antonio Cabral (Angola)
(Umbundu Translation)

V'imbo limwe vo Ngola mwakala ulume l'ukai. Vakwele, kwenda vakala ciwa. Ulume, pole, wakala lo ciuwa co kwendanda ko vyunda vyamale, ovoteke, oku kanyana olosanji, olohombo kwenda olongulu.

Eteke limwe uteke, watunda yapa. Omanu vosi v'imbo vapekela. Eye wapopolwila ko cunda camale yu atifa ko ohombo. Eci akapitila ko njo, ukai wo pula: "Eci wa cupapi he pi?"

Ulume wa kumbulula mo haeti: "Ukai wo cilombola kapula-pula".

Valale yapa. Va pasuka. Ko hombo yaco oyo va lyalya ko lyalye, toke eci ya kapwa.

Eteke l'ikavo oco. Uteke vo. Ulume wa tunda vali. O njanja eyi, wa nena ko ongulu. O ngulu yaco wa inena tupu yafa kwenda ya sukila omwenyo. Ukai wo pula vali: "Eci he ca tunda vali pi?"

135

The Road of the Gun
by Rafiq Sabir (Kurdistan)

I had a small blue sky
The occupiers brought it down over me
I had a little stream of dark blood,
a bundle of honey dreams
and a collection of books
they plundered them all.

But when they came
to change my skin
deform my face
I wore the snow and thunder
carried my homeland on my shoulders
and took to the road of the gun.

The King and The Shoes
by Abdul Karim Kassid (Iraq)

The first tale

Once upon a time the King's shoes went out for a stroll
And they returned and said to the King:
"We are worried about your security my Lord,
So we decided to stroll alone
the sleeping guards thought that we were
a passing squirrel or hedgehog
the streets bowed to us as we passed
The houses seemed to rise up in obedience to us
And the moon seemed on its guard."
Then they stood humbly between the feet of the King,
the King said:
"There is no blame on you
But be careful!
Of the revolt of commoners
And the slyness of the mob
I fear for you in the night
As you fear for me in the day."
The shoes were shining brightly
Until they shouted before the King:
"I am the sun."
From that day
the shoes went out at night
And slept in the day
Learning all the people's secrets
big and small
Nothing escaped them
Until the day the shoes became the King's crown
the King declared:
"My shoes
My crown."

The second tale

When the shoes became the crown
People were afraid
And stopped wearing shoes
they thought of shoes all the time
the oldest said:
"What shall we do?"
the youngest said:
"What shall we do?
Since the cold attacks us."
The shoes were shining
In the pictures on the walls
As if they were a sign of war
Or question marks
The shoes said: "My people"
Then they struck the King's head like a hammer.

The third tale

The shoes ruled justly for many years
though they disliked seeing the people
Since the people were all hungry
the people looked at the shoes
As the shoes had looked at the people before
Bare-footed and distressed,
Until they seemed empty
Faded...
headless
As if they were shoes of wax
As if they were a sun setting over the Kingdom
They had no splendour or glitter
But were shoes
Merely shoes.

At Last Raise Your Voice
by Diangitukwa Fweley (Zaire)

They are all from hell
   those who fold their arms
   when you say in unison
   We are hungry
They are all from hell
   those who turn on the taps
   and give you hot water
   when you are parched
They are all from hell
   those who throw you seeds
   to divide you
They are all from hell
   those who are well aware
   that you have an empty stomach
   but yet delight in verbosity
They are all from hell
   those who crush you
   in the public square
   to prove their greatness
They are all from hell
   all those who crucify us
   everyday

(Translated by Jennifer Langer)

The Children of Laç Deresi
by *Munzur Gem (Kurdistan)*

It was a hot summer day. The sky had become a scorching red-hot griddle, and it seemed as though the golden rays of the sun were pouring fire down on the earth.

That year war had come to Dersim and Laç Deresi had been under siege for many days. So many soldiers gathered together had never been seen or heard there before. There were sounds of gunfire and explosions and dust-clouds accumulated in mounds. As fighting intensified here and there the sounds of gunfire and human voices mingled. For days the Kurdish fighters and the military had been engaged in a pitiless struggle to the death.

The Turkish commander, directing his unit as he leant against a rock at the base of one of the hill-cliffs, was utterly exhausted. His knees had no more strength and his tired legs could hardly support his body.

Now and then he shivered as his eye lighted on two Kurdish children about fifteen or twenty paces away from him. For a moment he quite forgot the burden of tiredness that oppressed him and began to look at them strangely.

Each of the children was carrying a wooden stick and watching the battlefield. Their eyes never left it for a moment. Holding their sticks like guns, they kept taking aim and darting back and forward as though avoiding bullets. It did not even cross their minds that they were captives in the hands of the enemy. Their whole attention was on the fighting in the stream below. Sometimes they laughed, or sometimes frowned. Occasionally they said something to each other but the Turkish officer could not understand them. For the first time since his arrival in Dersim he wished he knew Kurdish. "That would be useful," he said to himself.

At the same moment, blinking his bloodshot eyes several times and stroking his chin, he summoned one of Der-

140

sim's inhabitants, Milis Ali. Ali approached fearfully, as he always did.

"Here, sir," he said.

The officer indicated the children.

"Look at that! What about that!" he said.

Ali looked where he pointed and when he saw the children his heart sank and momentarily his mind went blank. He could not think straight or control his confusion. He was quite unable to collect his wits. He turned to the officer and said, his voice trembling,

"I see them, sir."

The officer took a few angry steps towards him.

"And what are they doing? Do you see what they're doing?" he asked.

Under his heavy moustache riddled with white, Ali's mouth opened fearfully and with difficulty and he answered again in a trembling voice.

"Yes, sir, I see."

Then the officer continued,

"Very well. Now go and tell them what I say. We want to take them both away and look after them. It's our aim to free them from these mountain tops. They will become educated men. And when they grow up they'll become rich and possess property. They know perfectly well there's no life on these mountain tops. Besides, there's a battle going on just down there, the stream is overflowing with dead bodies. Most of the bandits are dead; few are left and they haven't much of a chance. I want to ask them this: would they prefer to stay with us or go back there?"

"Yes, sir," Ali replied.

He turned round to the children and repeated word for word what the Turkish officer had said. Their eyes gleamed as they listened to Ali. When he had finished, the slightly older one spoke:

"We don't want to stay here. Please ask him to let us go and we'll be off. That's all we ask, to go back down to our own people again."

Glancing down at the stream, the child continued:

141

"What have we got left in this world? Everything we possess is in the valley. All we care about is in Laç Deresi. We want to go and die there like our fathers and mothers! At least our dead bodies will be beside them."

At first Ali tried to dissuade them but the children refused to listen. They were stubborn as mules and when they remained indifferent, he translated their words to the officer. He laughed aloud. But it was cold meaningless laughter. Then he drew a deep breath and noisely cleared his throat. Once more an unfeeling voice emerged.

"The viper's young has venom too." What a true saying! "Very well, let them go down to the stream since that's what they want. Sometimes we are grieved for you and pity you. You can never be men. It's not possible that you Kurds will ever see reason. So you must be cut off at the root — there's no other way, no other solution. They can say what they like, this is my own view," said the officer, and throwing a word over his shoulder, he added, "Tell them they can go."

Ali did not know what to say. It crossed his mind to speak to the children again and perhaps dissuade them, but he immediately abandoned the idea. He was sure it would be no good. Instead he translated the officer's words for them.

At first the children could not believe him. Was the Turkish officer really such a good man? He didn't have this idea before, why now? So they asked:

"In God's name, are you telling the truth?"

"It is the truth. From this moment you are free. Waste no time," said Ali.

Like an arrow from the bow, the children shot off and began to run straight towards the valley of death. But their joy did not last. At the officer's command, the rifles fired and in Laç Deresi, two more children suddenly fell bleeding to the ground.

Milis Ali's eye was now fixed on the blood which flowed and soaked into the earth and he did not even hear the Turkish officer's last words.

"They got what they deserved. What does it matter?" he had said.

Experiences of War in the Home Country

Kazenga

Antonio Joaquim Marques (Angola)

And the tin house is invaded
By the pleasure of music
Unconciliatory voices choking
In vain forgotten dreams
Disputes and rebukes over glasses of beer
Faces at variance with each other
Elucidating despair in every gesture
But the music invites indulgence
And the occasion responds
With Kanjica with mufete
And funji with dry fish in hot sauce
Oh the music invites hope
And the dance syncopates now
In the girl's wriggling waist
And Kalunga's ecstatic eyes are fireflies
And the smell of sweat coagulates the air
The movements of bodies punctuating
And oh the scent of sex as the music growls
Suspicion erupts at first glances
Raising disturbing questions of the day:
Who is stealing somebody's wife?
Who is the sorcerer, why did Mbele die?
Why was the Minister smiling nervously on TV?
And the answer is muffled in exasperation
Of everyone talking without listening
The elements of purpose are deviated
The truth is muffled with fear of betrayal

And now the smoke of tobacco
The semba and the kabetula dance
The chattering and the gossipping
Deprecating laughter pours in once in a while
Provoking the stubborness of raw-rapprochment
And the sun lumbers west in resignation with music
The evening interferes with the day
A charcoal light lamp intercedes
And it's time for everyone to go home now
To face the nightmare of a country at war
With itself.

Notes:
Kazenga = A township in Luanda — Angola
Kanjica, mufete, funji = traditional Kimbundu ethnic foods
Semba = A dance of the navel from which Samba of Brazil originated
Kabetula = Folk dance (Luanda)

September, Beginning of the Winter
by Igor Klikovac (Bosnia)

As I saw bright remains of the fire extinguishing foam
which was hugging the burnt skeleton of the neighbouring
skyscraper
with the confidence of snow, suddenly I felt
an abandonment, which can only be compared with
the destiny of a coin withdrawn from circulation.

This year reality quotes its price
condescendingly, like a tradesman. Imperceptibly it casts
a shadow like that left on smoker's lungs
by a scrounged cigarette.

Operation Water Reservoir
by Ahmed Omar Askar (Somalia)

The soldiers rushed into two flanks in opposite directions
and in a few minutes the village was surrounded. Sergeant
Godgod and his friend Lugogod dashed into the village
instead of going with the other soldiers. They had to be
there for the hunt for gold, before anybody else. They ran
down the only street in the village. Godgod in the lead. As
he ran, he turned his head from side to side, looking for a
glimpse of a woman. When he saw a woman disappear into
one of the huts he shouted to his friend. "Let us go to that
hut, a woman has just entered it. She was wearing nice
clothes; she must be rich." They reached the hut and
rushed in with drawn guns. The woman seeing the two soldiers with their guns pointed at her, uttered a loud cry.
Sergeant Godgod slapped her hard on the face. Her one-
year-old child was sleeping on the floor and the startled
child crawled towards its mother. The mother scooped the
child into her arms and pressed it to her breasts, sobbing
in terror. "Guard her and do not let her make the slightest movement. I will search the hut," said Godgod.

He started turning everything upside down and inside
out. He turned over the mats but there was nothing under
them. He tore the pillow open and flung its contents onto
the floor. He could not find any gold in that either. He saw
a wooden box in one corner of the hut. That would contain
all her important possessions, he thought. Hurriedly he
carried the box to the centre of the hut. It was locked. He
prised it open with his bayonet. He lifted the lid off the box
and started throwing its contents onto the floor. He
opened a tin and on finding that it only contained some
incense, he threw it away. A small cloth bag caught his
eye. He immediately picked it up and he could feel that it
contained jewels. He opened it and poured its contents
onto his palm. His eyes lit up at the sight of the gold.
Greedily he gazed at the golden necklace and at the two

earrings in his hand. The woman in her desperate plight had collected her wits and said "Please don't take that gold, it's all I've got in the world."

Godgod lunged at her with the butt of his gun and hit her hard on the jaw. The woman and the child collapsed on the floor. He shouted to his friend, "Let's get out of here." The two soldiers emerged from the hut leaving the child crying over its unconscious mother. They met up with their friends in the street who were guarding the villagers who were now their prisoners. Nearby lay a collection of loot, sacks of food, clothes, cooking utensils and water pots. They had no intention of leaving anything of value in the huts before setting them ablaze. This was a disappointment for Sergeant Godgod and Corporal Lugogod. There was nothing left to loot. Their friends had made a neat job of it. They had wasted their time on one hut. "We were slow in searching that hut. The other soldiers had better opportunities than us. They have looted all the money from the teashops," said Godgod.

The first explosion from the water reservoir shook the ground. Water and earth erupted into the sky like a volcano. The wet particles from the blast obscured the skyline of the village. The blast cleared slowly. The villagers knew they were blowing up their water reservoir, the most precious thing in their lives but they could not defend themselves whilst sitting in the hot sun in rows, surrounded by the soldiers. The blasts continued mushrooming over the village one after the other, until all the water reservoirs had been destroyed. The villagers were counting the number of blasts and judging from the direction of the explosions which water reservoir was being destroyed. Dego Bayr returned from the direction of the water reservoirs and shouted orders to his soldiers. "Take the prisoners and the loot to the trucks and burn all the huts in the village."

The soldiers drove their prisoners to the trucks and some of them laboured under the weight of the loot. Godgod and Lugogod ran to burn the village. They poured

147

petrol on one hut in every street and then set fire to them. The soldiers then left the burning village to join the others who were doing the same job in the next village.

That day Saleban Ugas had taken his camels to the distant hills which lay eastwards of Tuulo Buur, his home village. Herding camels being a most difficult job for a nomad, he was wandering with them to make sure they did not stray. It was the breeding season and the large camel was after the she-camels, not giving them a chance to feed. He was also driving the younger camels away from the herd.

At noon when the herd was feeding peacefully, Saleban sat in the shade of a tree to rest his aching feet. Suddenly the thunder of a distant explosion brought him to his feet. Frightened, the camels ran up the hill. He pursued them until he managed to stop them at the top. From there, he could see a grey cloud over his village where the explosion had occurred. Another explosion followed. He could clearly see the smoke mushrooming over the village.

A sudden wave of alarm ran through his whole body. He felt he had to get to the village without delay. He had left his one-year-old child and wife there. He started driving his camels home as explosions continued in quick succession. The camels were rushing back and he had to stop them with quick lashes of his long stick. The narrow path, along which he drove the camels, zigzagged between patches of acacia tree and then rose over the hill. From the top of the hill, he could see that his village was ablaze. He rubbed his eyes and then looked again at the burning village. It was reality — dense smoke hung over it like a cloud and the flames looked like an infernal fire.

Leaving the camels, he ran down the hill towards the village, regardless of the thorny bushes tearing at his clothes and skin as he brushed against their branches. Finally he reached the open land of the village. He continued running, turning right to reach the tarmac road since the direct route to the hut had been blocked by the fire. He could now see that the fire had not yet reached the hut but

148

the flames had started to lick the adjacent one. He ran down the road like the wind, arriving at his hut gasping.

At the door he heard his child crying and hurried inside. He found his wife lying on the floor holding the child to her breasts. She was conscious but too weak to move. He said "We must get out of here. Can you walk?" "If you support me," she said weakly.

He lifted the child into his arms and told his wife to lean on his shoulder. Painfully she rose to her feet and leaning on him, they walked away from the flames to the bushes. There Saleban told his wife to sit down for a while so that they could rest before continuing their slow walk. She sat slowly on the ground while he seated himself on a rock and asked; "Who set fire to our village? Where is everybody?" "The soldiers." "Which soldiers?" "The military."

She started sobbing and it was hard to question her any further. He had to make a decision. Their only chance lay in crossing the border into Ethiopia at night.

Pulu Pulu — "The Runs"
by *Mabiala Molu (Zaire)*

Mmh, Mmh, Mmh
Grr, grr, Grr
Aah, aah, aah!
Zzz, zzz, zzz!
Bokomona mbula oyo! (You will experience it this year!)
"Ndoki aboki na mboka" ("A sorcerer is amongst us in the country.")

Ooh, ooh, ooh!
Uuh, uuh, uuh!
???, ???, ???!
$$$, $$$, $
Oo+,00+,00+!
Bokomela mayi na tonga! (You will quench your thirst through a syringe)
"Ndoki abomi bato na nzala" ("A sorcerer has made people starve to death.")

Prr, prr, prr!
Ptt, ptt, ptt!
Ppu, ppu, ppu!
Wxz, wxz, wxz!
Bokoliano mbula oyo! (You will cannibalise yourselves)
"Ndoki apelisi moto na mboka" ("A sorcerer has set the country alight!")

(Translation from Lingala by Jean-Marie Witele)

150

A Spectacle
by Sadiq al-Saygh (Iraq)

Sir, the windows
are blocked with mud
and the eaves of the minarets
shake for the worshippers.
Under the sun, time mends the garment of life.
Blood is still on the walls, death behind the teeth.
The unknown murderer is still monster of the night
and man lies sprawled
on the cold asphalt.

Sarajevo
by Semezdin Mehmedinovic (Bosnia)
1. Death by Freezing

When Sarajevo lies covered with snow, when pine trees are cracked by frost, bones in the earth will feel warmer than us. People will freeze to death: a fireless winter approaches, a sunless summer is past. The nights are already cold and, when somebody's pet dog barks from a balcony, a chorus of strays barks back, in tones as sorrowful as a crying child's. Only in this city does an Irish setter— normally an unusually cheeky dog — howl dismally in the night like Rutger Hauer in the final scenes of *Blade Runner*. Snow will bury the city as war has buried time. What day is it today? When is Saturday? I don't know. The daily and annual rituals are dead. Who will print calendars for 1993 in December? There is day, there is night; within them there is a man whose existence is defined by the end of the world. He knows that the fulness of life would be diminished were it not for the looming global catastrophe. Therefore he strikes a light at dusk; a wick threaded throught a metal ballpoint refill, fixed to a piece of cork wrapped in tin foil, so that it floats on the surface of the cooking oil which burns in a lamp made of an empty beer can. The cheerful flame allows him to see that objects and the faces of dear ones have an earthly glow; and that there is no plight but the failing of light.

2. Wounded Parks

Driven by fear of winter, the inhabitants of Sarajevo have been felling trees in the parks. The prevailing sound in the city, apart from that of shelling, is the noise of chain-saws. Everyday scenes: men pulling at a wire rope, the poplar resists, swings to and fro, children run around it, some cheering the men on, some rooting for the poplar, and when the crown has fallen the view opens on to the woods of Mr Trebevic, a very tall man, with neatly cut greying hair, in a new lustrous suit and shiny shoes, bow-tied, carrying a briefcase in his left hand, and in his right, a hefty chestnut branch chopped off in a park. He drags it with difficulty through the street door.

"The city's trees are under attack. They are being felled in parks, in the streets, even in cemeteries. We call on all citizens to protect the city's trees. Failure to comply will incur severe punishment." These lines from a daily newspaper tell me that if I fail to protect the city's trees, too busy with my own affairs, I shall be severely punished. Nevertheless the plaintive wailing of a chain-saw is heard to the north. People in the city are desperate, as thin creatures always are at the approach of winter.

3. Chetnik Positions

First the excavator arrived. It dug trenches in the ground and a lorry brought concrete slabs to line them with. Tanks were dug in at the sides so that only their cannon protruded. Guns as well. Our rifles cannot reach them. Perhaps they could spend the winter in such trenches? It is August now; they get tobacco from Nis, brandy from Prokuplje. I don't know where their women come from but I have seen them through binoculars. One of them has placed an inflatable mattress by the trench and is sunbathing in a swimsuit. She lies there for hours. Then she gets up, goes to the cannon, pulls the cord and fires a shell on the town at random. She listens briefly for the explosion and watches for its source. She even stands on tiptoe innocently. Then she goes back, coats her body with suntan lotion, and surrenders herself to serenity.

Dialogue
by Hadi Khorsandi (Iran)

A-Could you sign here, please?

And here.

Another signature here, please.

Could I have your finger-prints here, please? And two photocopies of your identity card, please.

B-Here you are, two photocopies of my identity card.

A-Two passport-size photographs, without glasses?

B-Here you are.

A-Certificate of good conduct?

B-Here you are.

A-Have you got a recommendation from your revolution-ary komiteh?

B-Yes sir, here it is.

A-And you have brought along photographs of all your family's identity cards, haven't you?

B-Yes sir, I have.

A-Do you have a driving licence?

A-No sir, I haven't got a car. I've got a moped.

A-The engine number, frame number, your licence to ride a moped, the insurance cover of the moped, its registration certificate, and road tax receipt!

B-One moment sir, and I'll hand over all of them... Ah, there you are, I've got all of them ready.

A-Who fought alongside the Imam in 1963?

B-Tayyeb, sir, Tayyeb Haj-Rezai.

A-What was the name of the head of the revolutionary komiteh based at the American Embassy when the American spies were taken hostage?

B- Mashallah the Butcher.

A-What was the occupation of the man who assassinated Razmara?

B-He was a carpenter.

July the Fourth 1991
by Sasa Skenderija (Bosnia)

I bought Boris a mouth organ for his birthday,
the same as I got when I was ten,
only orange. There's a war on: channel one
has news from the front, on two
it's the Wimbledon semi-finals. Now and again
transport planes rattle the window panes,
when they vanish into the horizon, that'll be
Slovenia. It's no bloody joke, say the old, no good'll
come of this. In the next room Boris is
learning the notes of the national anthem;
flies are squidging the remains of the banana
birthday cake.

Kupio sam Borisu melodiku rodjendan,
onaku kakvu sam ja dubio sa svoj deserti,
samo narancastu. Rat je i na prvom
programu su vijesti s fronte, na drugom
wimbledonsko polufinale. Svako malo
transporteri zatresu ptozorska stakla,
tamo gdje nestaju u obzorju je Slovenija
valjda. Nije zajebancija, kaze stari, ovo
nece na dobro. U sus jednoj sobi Boris na
melodici uvjezbava taktove drzavne himne;
muhe se lijepe na ostatke rodjendanske
torte od banana.

(Croatian)

Bombardment
by Mohammed Khaki (Kurdistan)

Ex...plo...sion
A child's severed arm flying
Delicate deer legs breaking
Poor butterfly through the dust crawling

Ex...plo...sion
Houses collapsing
Schools flattened
Corn alight with a thousand burning nests.
Bridges blasted
City destroyed, in ruins.
Explosion
 groaning
  wailing
   agony
Nearby the wireless bulletin howls "success!"
"Enemy target attacked and destroyed."

Further Reading

Edges of Poetry: Selected Poems by *E. Kho'i,* 1995, Blue Lagos Press (Santa Monica)
The Flying Bosnian by *Miroslav Jancic*, 1996, Hearing Eye
Anthology of Contemporary Kurdish Poetry, 1994, Kurdish Solidarity and Yashar Ismail
Through the Vast Halls of Memory by *Haifa Zangana,* 1991, Hourglass
A Gob Tree Beside the Hargeisa Wadi by *Abdirahman Mirreh*, 1995, Tuba Press
From an Acacia Landscape by *Abdirahman Mirreh,* 1996, Haan
Songs of a Nomad Son by *Abdirahman Mirreh,* 1990, Tuba Press
Aujourd'hui Le Soleil by *Mabiala Molu,* Universal Connection, Paris
Klaonica edited by *Ken Smith and Judi Benson,* 1993, Bloodaxe Books
In the Name of our Fathers by *Abdirazak Y. Osman*, 1996, Haan
Stories by Iranian Women Since the Revolution, 1991, Center for Middle Eastern Studies, University of Texas
Storm, Out of Yugoslavia, 1994, Storm
Stone Soup, No 1, 1995, edited by *Igor Klikovac and Ken Smith*
Hal-Abuur, Vol 1, Nos 2 and 3, 1993/4
Les Etoiles Ecrasées by *Pius Ngandu Nkashama*, 1990, Editions Publisud, Paris
Index on Censorship
Sharks and Soldiers by *Ahmed Omar Askar*, 1992, distributed by Haan Associates
Couronne d'Epines by *Diangitukwa Fweley*, 1985, Editions Saint-Germain-des-Prés, Paris
Erewhon, 1994, *Stichting Ex-Yu* PEN, Amsterdam
Souffle, Collection "Poésie Toujours", by *Cikuru Batu-*

mike, Editions Saint-Germain-des-Prés, Paris
The Ayatollah and I: New Iranian Satire by *Hadi Khorsandi,* 1987, Readers International
Zlata's Diary by *Zlata Filipovic,* 1994, Penguin

Zaire/Democratic Republic of Congo

Literary/Cultural background

The languages of Zaire are French, Lingala, Kikongo, Kiswahili and Ciluba.

Kikongo literature

Up to World War 2, Kikongo was the main language used for literature.

When the Congo became the personal empire of Leopold II, King of the Belgians, in 1885, Protestant missionaries managed to establish a few stations and schools where the Kikongo language was used for teaching Scripture. For several decades, Kikongo literature consisted mainly of Protestant hymns. A new trend emerged after World War 1, when the followers of the religious leader, Simon Kimbangu (1889-1951), started composing hymns reflecting their own creed.

The first Kikongo novelists were Emile Disengomoko (1915-1965) and Jacques N. Bahele (b. 1911). Other writers of prose fiction were Andre Massaki and Noe Diawaky. The most prolific Kongo writer in independent Zaire is A. Fikiau Kia Bunseki (b. 1934), whose chief contribution to imaginative writing is Dongo-Dingo (1966) which is a collection of seven long poems giving the traditional pre-Christian Kongo world view. Basically, the two main trends in Kikongo literature were hymn writing and prose fiction. An important outlet for Kongo writing disappeared in 1973, when the Zairean government banned all missionary periodicals as part of a policy designed to strengthen its control over the press and other media. It is, therefore, quite possible that the short term future may see Kongo lose its literary predominance among Zairean languages.

The other main local languages have not been used for literature. Current Zairean policy is a determination to bolster national unity by spreading Lingala which is now the language of the political and administrative leadership. This official support may lead to creative writing in Lingala. The Zairean government has given four Bantu languages special status as national languages. They are Lingala, Kiswahili, Kikongo and Ciluba. For generations, Bantu speakers have passed on their wisdom and traditional values through storytelling. In recent decades, efforts have been made to write down the stories and legends.

Literature in French

It was not until World War 2 that writing in French began to emerge in Zaire. This was because the school system, which was the responsibility of Catholic missionaries working in close co-operation with the colonial administration, spread a minimal degree of literacy. After World War 2, a process of liberalisation started. In the two decades following World War 2, there were three main currents in literature: ethnographic (works inspired by folk tales, legends and poems from the oral tradition), *litterature de ténoignage* (based on historical events, personal experiences and memories) and poems and fiction inspired by the Négritude movement: the search for cultural identity, authenticity and a return to traditional forms and techniques. A magazine called *La Voix du Congolais,* was launched in 1945 and offered educated Congolese an opportunity to express their views. The editor, Antoine-Roger Bolamba (b. 1913), wrote *Esanzo, Chants pour mon Pays* (1955, *Songs for my Country*), which drew upon ancient Bantu tales. It was the first Zairean literacy work to be published in Paris. Antoine-Roger Bolamba was the main voice of protest against the evils of Belgian colonization. Paul Lomami-Tschibamba (b. 1914) won a Belgian literary prize for his novel *Ngando* (1948, *The Crocodile*) which was published in Brussels.

The Congo became independent in 1960. The early years of independence were marked by political crises, army mutinies and civil wars leading to Colonel Mobutu's *coup d'état*. This affected literary creativity with individual liberty and free speech almost non-existent and arbitrary detentions common. However, later, independence inspired Zairean authors with new themes which were expressed in political writings and historical accounts. A number of poetry clubs were formed by young intellectuals headed by Clementine Nzuji, one of the first African women poets writing in French.

Between 1965 and 1970, poetry flourished and mostly expressed the pessimism and disillusion of the 1960s. In 1971, V.Y. Mudimbe, possibly Zaire's greatest contemporary writer, founded *Editions Mont Noir,* offering another outlet for the publication of poetry. Although there was intense theatrical activity in Zaire, few plays have actually been published. The founders of literary drama were Mobyem M.K. Mikanza (b. 1944) and P. Ngandu Nkashama (b. 1946), whose *La Delivrance d'Ilunga* (1977, *The Freeing of Ilunga*), extols the values of freedom. In the 1970s, Lisembe Elebe produced plays about striking workers and village life and the career of Simon Kimbangu.

Zairean novelists such as Dieudonne Mutambo, Mbwil a Mpang Ngal and Vumbi Yoka Mudimbe, choose topics that range from the history of the independence movement to the demands of urban existence. Mudimbe's work expresses the suffering of a whole people, for whom he makes himself the mouthpiece. Several novelists write about present day Zairean society while others concentrate on the psychological and ethical problems connected with the despotism and corruption of many newly independent African states.

162

Clearly, historical/political events have had a strong influence on writers' themes and expression. Sony Labou Tansi (b. 1947) was a gifted writer who published plays and several novels. His first novel *La Vie et Demie* (1979) was awarded a literary prize and is a grotesque fable of the King Ubus of contemporary Africa. He died of AIDS in 1995.

Most Zairean authors write in French and have their works published in Belgium or France. This is because assimilationist attitudes and directives caused the emergence of a detribalised literature. Literature in vernacular languages is very limited in output.

Zairean writers in exile

When Mobutu was in power, many writers left Zaire and are dispersed mainly in France, Belgium, Switzerland and Germany. Brussels is now a major centre for revitalised central African culture. Maurice Boykasse, the head of the Libili theatre, is a poet, actor, storyteller and musician. He has written a musical about Africans who died for the cause of Catholicism in the Buganda Kingdom. Amongst these writers is Pius Ngandu Nkashama who was born in Zaire in 1946, and is now a professor at the University of Limoges in France. He is a major poet, essayist, novelist and playwright. Writers in exile often express negativity, pessimism and despair in narratives dealing with conflicts between individuals and authority, tradition and modernity, men and women and which expose widespread corruption, oppression and torture.

Further Reading

Zaire published by Lerner Publications Co., Minneapolis, USA, 1992
African Literatures in the Twentieth Century by *L.S. Klein*, 1988, Oldcastle Books

African Language Literatures by *Albert Gerard,* 1981, Longman
Black Art: Magazine Culturel des Mondes Noires, France (Autumn 1995 edition)
Bulletin of Francophone Africa, (Autumn 1995), University of Westminster, Francophone Africa Research Centre
African Literature in the Twentieth Century by *O.R. Dathorne*, 1975, Heinemann

Political/historical background

Zaire was known as the Congo Free State and then The Congo. In 1971 the name of the country became Zaire, from the Bantu word "nzari" meaning river. In 1997, the name was changed to Democratic Republic of Congo.

Pre-independence
In 1885 the Congo Free State became the personal property of Leopold II. The capital of Zaire, Kinshasa, was formerly known as Leopoldville. In 1908 it became a Belgian colony called the Belgian Congo. The country's resources (copper, tin, cobalt, rubber, ivory, etc.) and its people, were exploited and the Congolese grew deeply dissatisfied with colonial rule. In 1956 the Alliance of the Kongo People insisted that the colonial government immediately provide rights of free speech, free association and freedom of the press as well as a long-term programme of political reform. Although Belgium did not grant these rights, the movement of national independence gained strength. Lumumba, who headed the multi-ethnic National Congolese Movement (MNC), called for full independence which was finally granted in 1960 in an atmosphere of distrust between the new government and Belgium.

Post-independence
Joseph Kasavubu, the ABAKO leader, became president and Lumumba became prime minister. In July sections of

the Congolese army mutinied against its Belgian officers. As violence spread, Europeans fled the country. Lumumba dismissed the Belgian army commander and appointed Mobutu army chief of staff. At the same time, conflict was brewing in the copper-rich southern region of Katanga (Shaba) and Katanga was declared independent by its leader Tschombe. The Congolese army put down another attempted secession in Kasai but failed to make any impression on Katanga. Lumumba and Kasavubu fell out, tried to dismiss each other but were both dismissed by Mobutu in an army *coup d'etat*. Lumumba escaped but was recaptured and eventually murdered.

Turmoil followed the death of Lumumba. The regions of East Kasai and Kivu asserted their independence and the civil war continued. Finally Katanga was restored to the Congo Republic but civil war continued in West Kasai, East Kasai and Kivu. Kasavubu invited Tschombe to return and serve as prime minister but then dismissed him and Colonel Mobutu ousted Kasavubu in a non-violent take-over.

Mobutu

Mobutu established his control throughout the country. He nationalised the huge Belgian company that controlled the Congo Republic's copper production. He exiled Tschombe and further weakened the opposition by pitting ethnic groups against each other. In the 1970 elections, Mobutu made his party (MPR), the country's sole legal political party.

Zaire struggled economically in the mid 1970s and in 1977 and 1978 Katangan rebels based in Angola, attacked Shaba. Zaire's problems continued throughout the 1980s. The annual inflation rate reached 100% and the standard of living continued to decline. Throughout 1991, Zaire was unstable politically. Riots erupted in Kinshasa where unpaid soldiers looted stores and destroyed property. Food shortages occurred followed by a decline in medical supplies. In autumn 1991, Mobutu agreed to rule with the help of a cabinet dominated by opposition leaders.

Tshisekedi became the country's prime minister but was soon dismissed by Mobutu. He tried to replace Tshisekedi's administration with the MPR but they refused to step down. In June 1994 a new transitional government was formed with the centrist opposition leader Kengo wa Dondo as prime minister. Tshisekedi and his UDPS party refused to participate in the government.

In 1996 there was fighting between ethnic Tutsis and Zairean troops.

In October 1996, up to 300,000 refugees were on the move in eastern Zaire as Hutus tried to avoid being caught up in battles between Zairean troops and ethnic Tutsis from Zaire. Zairean villagers fled the fighting as well as about 220,000 Hutu refugees from Rwanda and Burundi.

Zaire was a country of terror and brutality where human rights were abused and where law and order had broken down. Death squads had the power to torture and kill. Zaireans were leaving the country because it was too insecure and dangerous. By 1996 Mobutu had ruled for 31 years.

In 1996/7 a rebellion against the government, led by Laurent Kabila, was finally victorious after horrific bloodshed. Laurent Kabila is now the president.

Iran

Literary/Cultural Background

The language of Iran is Farsi.

Iran has a tradition of classical literature and poetry which is a thousand years old. Blending recollections of pre-Islamic literature with Moslem culture, poetry is not only the most accomplished of Iranian arts, it has also preserved the continuity of the Persian language. Some of the great poets of medieval Persia were Ferdowsi, Khayyam, Sa'di, Rumi and Hafez. From the fifteenth to the nineteenth centuries, poetry was written in this classical tradition. Poetry became very opulent and ornamented in phraseology, but generally devoid of substance and original thought. Modern Persian poetry developed through the influence of poets from the West, such as Pound and Hopkins and was at first bitterly condemned as heresy but later a cult was made of it.

The Iranian imperial system had always shown complete intolerance in any form of expression which it had not inspired itself or which could develop independently of it. The Shahs always tried to suppress all forms of thought which questioned their authority. Throughout Persian history, revolutionary or controversial poets suffered imperial censorship, banishment and assassination. A characteristic of Persian culture was the continual antagonism between the imperial system and popular expression. As the true undisguised description of reality in Iran had always been dangerous, symbolism and allegory, used as a camouflage, soon become a predominant trait of popular culture. In general, apart from two brief periods when constitutional law was respected and, therefore, freedom of expression flourished, creativity has always been suppressed in Iran. From 1909 to 1921, written Persian poetry and literature gradually freed itself from the sole duty of having to extol imperial magnificence. "New Poetry" was conceived during this period with poets such as Nezam-e-Vafa and Nima Youshidj. New writers were Moshfegh and Dehkhoda. For the first time in Iranian history, writers, poets and scholars openly politicised their work and social criticism began to be freely and challengingly expressed.

The end of democratic government in 1953 affected writers. Press censorship became intense and book censorship was introduced in 1960. Iranian cultural values were also undermined by American values at this time as Iranian cultural values were represented as retrograde while Western values were considered progressive. The Shah's regime denied an official licence to the Writers' Association because its members refused to join the Rastakhiz Party. In 1970, the Savak (Shah's secret police), started to harass and persecute and arrest members of the Writers' Association. Twenty-two leading novelists, poets and film-makers had already been imprisoned for being critical of the government. In 1977 the Shah was forced by the USA to declare an "Open Political Atmosphere" and letters signed by literary and cultural personalities were sent to the prime minister demanding that the government observe the human right of freedom of expression. The "Ten Nights of Poetry" in 1977 came to be regarded by many as one of the first sparks which ignited the 1979 revolution.

After the 1979 revolution in which the Shah was overthrown, an Islamic regime came to power. While most writers celebrated the revolution and the downfall of the Shah, they soon became disillusioned with the Islamic Republic. This regime believed that the only true knowledge had been produced by the prophets and the imams so that whole centuries of struggle by scholars and thinkers was dubbed as deviation or heresy. The regime was anticulture and did its utmost to suppress freedom of expression. In 1978, Khomeini referred to Iranian intellectuals and writers as agents of the Shah and lackeys of the super powers and had warned the faithful to steer clear of their influence.

Censorship was used as an instrument of suppression. Radio and television were censored when the Islamic Republic came to power. Forty newspapers were banned and an Islamic committee took over the main newspaper *Kayhan.* A large number of its journalists were dismissed and the editor was arrested and executed. Theatres were appropriated and used for speeches by mullahs. Gradually, theatrical performances were banned completely. Film censorship and new restrictive rules for film production were even harsher than for the theatre. Books, bookstores and libraries were banned and ancient and respected works such as Ferdowsi's *Shanameh,* were declared heretical. Printing houses were searched without warning.

The Iranian Writers' Association stood firm in defending freedom of expression and protested against incidents of censorship. However, eventually the Association was closed down by force and its members driven into hiding with considerable numbers being arrested, imprisoned, tortured and executed. One of these was Sa'eed Soltanpoor, the poet and playwright. A large number fled abroad. These included the poets, Mahmud Kianush, Esmail Kho'i, Ahmad Shamloo, the writers, Nasim Khaksar, Hadi Khorsandi. Currently, censorship is still in force and although some literary magazines are being published, these are devoid of any real discussion.

The writing of fiction by Iranian women is a recent development. For centuries men had the power of the pen and it was not until 1947 that the first collection of short stories by a woman, Simin Daneshvar, was published. According to Farzaneh Milani, the short-term effect of the Islamic Revolution has been dramatic and surprising, in that women have finally found an authentic voice in the novel and short story.

Further Reading

An Anthology of Modern Persian Poetry by *Ahmad Karimi-Hakkak* published by Westview Press, Boulder, Colorado, 1995

Index on Censorship

Stories by Iranian Women since the Revolution, Introduction by Farzaneh Milani, 1991, The University of Texas & University of Texas Press

Historical/Political Background

For over 2,500 years, Iran was a monarchy with the power in the hands of Shahs. Despite continuous persecution, the struggle for liberty never ceased. In 1906, a national uprising directed against the unlimited power of the Shah, demanded that the power of state be taken from the throne and given to the elected representatives of the people. The Emperor was forced to grant a constitution stipulating that freedom of expression and political liberty be guaranteed for all. However, barring two brief periods, this has never been respected.

In the early 1900s, undertakings and concessions had been concluded between the Shahs and Britain and Russia, weakening Persia's independence. In a perpetual state of near bankruptcy and military insignificance, Iran had become a no-man's land where the rivalry between England and Russia hindered economic, social and political development. Thus in 1907, Iran was divided into two spheres of influence, the north Russian and the south British. However, Mozaffar-al-Din Shah's sudden death in 1907 brought his son Mohammad-Ali to the throne and upset the Anglo-Russian balance of power in Iran. Mohammad-Ali Shah declared his hostility to constitutional rule. Civil war finally broke out, ending in 1909 with Mohammad-Ali Shah's defeat and deposition in favour of his son, Ahmad Shah, and the restoration of parliamentary democracy. From 1909 to the military coup of 1921, Iran was governed according to constitutional law.

At the end of World War 1 Britain became the unrivalled power in Persia. Because of the growing importance of Persian oil, Britain made it known that it was determined to impose a lasting hegemony over Iran. In 1921 Reza Pahlavi overthrew the government and a reign of terror began. In 1925, the Kadjar dynasty was dissolved and Reza Pahlavi was proclaimed Emperor. From 1925 to 1941, Iran was ruled solely according to the Shah's dictatorial methods. With the outbreak of World War 2, Iran became the nerve-centre of Hitler's spy network in the Middle East. The allies invaded Iran in 1941 and forced Reza Shah to abdicate in favour of his son, Mohammad-Reza. The change of regime restored parliamentary rule, political parties and trade unions.

The Anglo-Iranian Oil Co had become a state within a state. The nations's main resource was drained by Britain with little profit to the Iranian people. From 1952 to 1953, Mossadegh, the new prime minister, nationalised the country's oil industry and expelled British technicians from Persia. Finally the Americans overthrew Mossadegh and brought the Shah back to Teheran (he had fled to Rome). The new military government undertook a ruthless witch-hunt of all anti-imperialist elements. The fall of Mossadegh put an end to democratic government and to national sovereignty. From 1953 onwards, the Shah began to grant ever-increasing powers to the army and to the SAVAK, the deadly efficient secret police. By 1960 massive arrests, unjustified detentions, institutionalised torture, military tribunals, prison murders and executions had become commonplace. In 1963, in violent reaction to the Shah's "White Revolution", a mass revolt broke out all over the country. The army was hastily called in to restore imperial law and order and more than four thousand people were killed in the three-day battles. Ayatollah Khomeini, a persistent critic of the Shah's regime, was arrested and exiled from Iran. Finally the Shah was overthrown in 1979.

Ayatollah Khomeini became the leader of the new Islamic Republic and Iran became a theocratic state with strict Islamic fundamentalist rules and severe punishment for those who deviated. No secular opposition was allowed. Despite opposition from within, the death of Khomeini and a costly war with Iraq (1980–88), the revolutionary regime remains in power. When Ayatollah Khomeini died, he was succeeded by Ayatollah Khameini and President Rafsanjani. The recent elections in 1997 offered no alternative to the theocratic system imposed by Ayatollah

172

Khomeini. Mohammed Khatami, the new president, is a former culture minister who was dismissed for his supposed 'liberalism.'

Further Reading

Index on Censorship, Winter 1974 — **Repression in Iran** by *Ahmad Faroughy*
The Constitution of Iran by *Asghar Schirazi*, 1996, Taurus

Somalia

Literary/Cultural Background

Literature has played a paramount role in the life of the Somali people. Nearly one and a half centuries ago, Sir Richard Burton visited Somalia and described the Somalis as a "nation of poets". Somali literature chronicles almost all significant historical events. It is the factual mirror of social reality in which the Somali finds an intimate representation of him/herself. This is probably one of the main reason for the Somalis' love of literature.

The oral heritage was of great importance. This was in keeping with the orientation of a nomadic people. Every elder was expected to hold an audience for hours with a speech richly laced with proverbs and quotations from famous poems and sayings. Similarly, if he was to command respect, he also had to be capable not only of composing striking impromptu verse in the various traditional styles, but also of reciting the classical works of famous authors. The classical form of poetry was called "gabay" and was chanted. Since, traditionally, this oral heritage was not preserved in writing, it required prodigious feats of memory. Poets in traditional Somali society were highly esteemed and their poetry was an unusually powerful medium of communication between people.

Some of the greatest classical poetry is by Mohamed Abdullah Hassan. Another famous Somali classical poet was Aw-Muuse Ismaaciil who lived in the 19th century. He wrote a moving piece of poetry which had the power to trigger off one of the fiercest traditional confrontations between two sub-clans. Another celebrated classical poet was Salan Carrabey who recited a poem (Oh kinsmen, stop the hostility!) to prevent a bloody war. Somali classical poetry had the power to bring about peace and start wars.

174

After World War 2, a new genre of love poetry called "belwo" emerged. This was a miniature form of the classical poem "gabay". This new form appealed to townspeople because it was brief and because it interpreted reality from their standpoint. Songs of this genre made their debut with the establishment of radio transmissions. Modern poets became frequent broadcasters. Even today the spoken word remains supreme because cassettes of old and new poems are being taped, copied and recopied by Somalis living in their own country or abroad.

The first Somali writer to have been in a position to reach an international audience was William J.F. Syad whose first volume of poetry *Khamsine* (1959) was published in Paris. The tradition of poetry continues with poets like 'Hadraawi' who is in exile in London. He was the leader of the opposition movement at the time of Siad Barre and was exiled in Ethiopia. His poems address political and social issues. A new form of poetry/song, "helo", appeals to the younger generation.

Traditionally, males have received recognition for writing poetry and have appeared at public forums. Women, however, have written poetry but because of the barriers in society, they have not had the opportunity to recite them. Women's poetry has had various functions — religious, ritual, work etc.

Other genres, such as prose fiction and theatre, have become important in contemporary urban society. Both of these were initiated by Axmed Cartan Xaange. Classical poetry no longer has an overwhelming appeal for town-dwelling Somalis or for the younger generation.

The official orthography for writing the Somali language was introduced in 1972 and this led to the rapid growth of a new readership. Somali literary life witnessed the birth of a new genre i.e. the novel and short story. The first full-length modern novel was *Maanafaay* by Maxamed D. Afrax and it was first serialised in a national daily. Serialisation of stories in the daily press became a popular literary tradition in Somalia. During the eighties, an increasing number of young story writers published numerous novelettes and several novels, mostly based on modern early romantic and social themes. Generally, however, apart from the works of Nuruddin Farah in English, Somali fiction writing is still at an early stage of development. Nuruddin Farah's first novel was *From a Crooked Rib* (1970) which deals with a woman's fate in Somalia. He has published five novels in total.

Since the late fifties and early sixties, Somali theatre has occupied a central position in the cultural life of Somali towns. It was the most popular form of entertainment and also used as a powerful tool of mass education. Axmed Cartan Xaange produced the first modern play in Somali entitled *Samawada*. It deals with the role of women in the struggle for independence in the period following World War 2. Generally the playwrights are men and women of the people, most of whom have little or no formal education.

However, the government has discouraged all kinds of literary creation outside its propaganda machinery. Artists' freedom of expression has been curbed and suppressed since the military regime came to power in 1969 and since the disruption of the country by tribal wars. The poet, Abdulle Rage Taraweh, who was accused of expressing anti-government opinions in his poetry, was imprisoned for many years. In January 1996, more than thirty singers, dancers and actors were arrested during a show. They were imprisoned for one night and then flogged by order of the Sharia courts. With the current civil war in Somalia, most writers, playwrights and poets are now in exile. London has become a centre of literary activity with a journal of Somali literature and culture — *Hal-Abuur* — being published. Exile and the change of environment has, of course, affected Somali literature.

Further Reading

Faces of Islam in African Literature by *K.W. Harrow*, 1991, Heinemann
Hal Abuur, Vol 1, Nos 2 and 3
African Language Literatures by *Albert Gerard*, 1981, Longman
A Tree for Poverty by *Margaret Laurence*, 1993, McMaster University Library Press
Anthology of Somali Poetry by *B.W. & S. Andrzejewski*, 1993, Indiana University Press

Historical/Political background

The Somali population is ethnically homogenous with one culture, language and religion — Islam. The people are divided into four main patrilineal clans: Isaaq, Dir, Darod and Hawiye.

Somalia achieved its liberation from the British and Italians in 1960 when the former Italian colony in the south and the British Protectorate in the north merged to form a republic. Each had adopted administrative systems derived from the practices of the respective colonies and it proved difficult to unite these into one system.

A military *coup d'etat* in 1969 replaced the democratically elected government and brought Marxist Socialism under President Siad Barre. After an abortive coup in 1978, following the Somali defeat in the war against Ethiopia, the Somali government was at war with opposition movements based on various clans. Fighting was particularly fierce in northern Somalia. Full-scale civil war broke out in May 1988 when Somali National Movement (SNM) forces attacked the military bases around the northern towns of Burao and Hargeisa. There is formal documentation outlining the Government's systematic policy of genocide towards the northern clan dating from many years before the war broke out. The Somali government's response to the attack was to turn their guns on the civilian population of the towns, whom they suspected of collaborating with the SNM. Massive destruction resulted, and thousands of civilians were killed. Generally, Siad Barre's cruel, totalitarian government set clans against each other as well as oppressing and committing atrocities against the Somali people.

In 1991, rebels of the United Somali Congress (USC) dominated by the Hawiye clan and General Aideed, ousted Siad Barre and his army in the south, while the army garrisons in the north surrendered to the SNM. In June 1991, the north declared the independent Somaliland Republic. However, civil war continued unabated in the south resulting in huge loss of life and bringing famine, disease and anarchy.

In 1992, the United Nations authorised use of all necessary means to secure humanitarian relief and the US led operation "Restore Hope" began its peace-keeping role in Somalia. The United Nations withdrew in 1995 and warfare between the armed clan factions continued with the main warlord being General Aideed. He was killed in August 1996. His son, Hussein Aideed was named as his successor and the tribal fighting continues.

Further Reading

Understanding Somalia by *I.M. Lewis,* 1993, Haan
ESOL Refugee Pack by Jennifer Langer, 1992, Haan

Kurdistan

Literary/Cultural Background

A variety of languages are spoken in Kurdistan. Kurmanji is spoken in Turkey, Syria, the Soviet Union and in the northern parts of the Kurdish speaking areas of Iraq and Iran. Roman script is used. Sorani is spoken in Iraq and in the central parts of the Kurdish speaking area of Iran. Arabic script is used.

In Turkey, the Kurdish language was and still is essentially forbidden. According to the 1982 constitution, no language prohibited by law can be used in the expression and diffusion of opinions. No person may publish a prohibited language.

Kurmanji has been cultivated almost entirely in exile. Many Kurds from Turkey came to the West as immigrant workers in the sixties and seventies. In their new environment, some of these became politically more aware and felt freer to express their identity. As a result, there has been a varied output of written material in Kurmanji published in exile. Iraqi Kurds have created an impressive literature and an adequate written language and a generation of Kurds now exists which has received its primary and secondary education in Kurdish. In Iran, the recent history of the Kurdish language has neither been as tragic as Turkey's nor as successful as in Iraq. Publications in Kurdish have seldom been allowed and were banned by the Islamic Republic. However in 1984 there was a change in official policy and since then, there have been a number of publications in Kurdish, a Kurdish publishing house has been set up and education in Kurdish is now permitted. However, contemporary sentiments must be cloaked in stereotyped imagery.

The Kurdish language has a symbolic value as it shows that the Kurds are an independent people with a history,

179

literature and culture of their own. However, there is a lack of a common linguistic code. However, satellite TV in Kurdish is helping to spread the Kurdish language by teaching Kurdish outside Turkey to refugees in exile.

Kurdish literature is very rich in folklore such as epic stories and ballads on the subject of life, philosophy and love. The oldest Kurdish literary works date back to the 11th and 12th centuries. In 1695, Ahmadi Khani (1650 to 1707) put into verse the romantic love epic *Mamuzi* after the classical Persian pattern. A revered classical, Kurdish poet from east Kudistan was Hemin. There has been a very strong oral tradition which is now being threatened by television, radio and war.

Currently, the underlying themes of Kurdish poetry are love for Kurdistan and the natural world of mountains, plains, river, flowers, sun, moon and stars; admiration and veneration of the Kurdish freedom fighters (Peshmergas), the male poets' love of women and the torment of unrequited love (due to feudal traditions, war or exile), the tragic loneliness of exile and the poets' overwhelmimg longing to see Kurdistan again; images of rage at the loss, destruction and brutality witnessed in the course of war, but at the same time, pride and honour in fighting for one's people and country.

The collapse of the Kurdish movement in Iraq in 1975 caused many Kurdish intellectuals to flee abroad.

In Turkey there has been victimisation of writers and journalists. The first editor of a pro-Kurdish daily was sentenced to twenty-five years in prison in 1995. Many jounalists and writers die in police custody or in prison.

A famous Kurdish nationalist poet is Sherko Bekas who was born in Iraqi Kurdistan and now lives in exile in Sweden. He published his first collection of poems in Baghdad in 1968 three years after joining the Kurdish liberation movement in 1965, working in the movement's radio station — The Voice of Kurdistan. During the period 1984 to 1987, he lived with the Kurdish peshmergas. Sherko Bekas attacks oppression with words. In 1987, he was presented with Sweden's Tokholoski prize for refugee poets from oppressed nations.

A well-known Kurdish writer from Turkey, who also lives in exile in Sweden, is Munzur Gem who writes fiction and short stories. He left Turkey in 1980.

Further Reading

Anthology of Contemporary Kurdish Poetry, 1994, Kurdistan Solidarity Committee
Kurdistan In Search of Ethnic Identity by *Turaj Atbaki and Margreet Dorleijn,* 1990, Hontsma Foundation
Silence is Killing Them, 1993, International Association for Human Rights in Kurdistan

Political/historical background

The name "Kurdistan" designates an area on the present borders of Turkey, Iran, Iraq and Syria, the homeland of the Kurds, a pastoral nomadic people of Indo-European origin. The Kurdish people are probably the only community of over 15 million people which does not have national statehood.

Kurds in Turkey

The Treaty of Sevres in 1920, contained provision for an independent state in Kurdistan although it was never ratified because Kemal Attaturk ensured that Turkish national interests dominated the final settlement of Turkey's borders in the Treaty of Lausanne in 1923. The Turkish government repressed the Kurdish population and there were Kurdish uprisings. Every effort was made to break down Kurdish identity and the old feudal-tribal relationships. Land was confiscated and chiefs and whole sections of tribes were transplanted with between 500,000 to a million Kurds being displaced. The Kurdish language was banned in 1925, including its teaching in schools and use in publications. Officially Kurds became known as "mountain Turks".

Since World War 2, official Turkish attitudes towards the Kurds have fluctuated with local political trends and events. In 1965, a clandestine Kurdistan Democratic Party, Turkey, was founded, allied to the KDP, Iraq. Like their Iraqi counterpart, the KDPT represented the more conservative separatist elements in Turkish Kurdish political life. Left-wing Kurds had opted to work within the framework of the Turkish Workers' Party (TWP) towards equal rights for Kurds in a reformed, democratic and socialist state. The proliferation of left-wing Kurdish groups in the 1960s drove the government to increase repression of Kurdish political groups. Political violence continued to increase throughout the 70s so martial law was proclaimed in the Kurdish provinces in 1979. Another military coup in 1980 meant even harsher repression of Kurdish identity and politics and suspected leftists and Kurdish nationalists were arrested, interrogated and tortured. In 1980, all parties, including the TWP, were banned.

Since the 1970s, a new generation of small separatist Kurdish parties has developed in Turkey and amongst Kurds in Europe e.g. the PKK which uses guerrilla tactics against Turkish security forces. A civilian government was restored in Turkey in 1983. The Political Parties Act (1983), however, made Kurdish political parties illegal and the use of Kurdish continued to be an offence. Amnesty International estimate that many thousands of Kurds have been tortured and killed by Turkish governments.

From 1993 to 1995, Turkey destroyed over 2000 Kurdish villages in the eastern Kurdish provinces, causing the mass migration of an estimated 4 million Kurdish refugees. In 1995, there was a massive military incursion by Turkey into the internationally protected area in Iraqi Kurdistan. The Turkish assault was allegedly aimed at wiping out the Kurdish liberation movement.

Kurds in Iran

As in Turkey, the post-World War 1 situation in Iran saw several separatist uprisings as local leaders took advantage of the loosening of central control. These were traditional revolts by ambitious tribal leaders but by the beginning of the Second World War, Reza Shah had successfully repressed all separatist movements. In 1941, the Russians and British occupied Iran. The Kurds, with the encouragement of the Soviets, were able in 1946 to set up an autonomous Kurdish republic — the Mahabad Republic. However, after the Iranian army took control, the leader, Qadhi Muhammad, and the other leaders were hung by the Iranians.

Between 1946 and 1979, Kurds in Iran suffered similar repressive measures to the Turkish Kurds. The conservative influence of Barzani and the Iraqi KDP persisted in the KDPI (Kurdish Democratic Party of Iran) of this period. Left-wing elements in the KDPI were refused help and some were murdered by the Iraqi KDP as part of their bargain with the Shah for aid against the Ba'thist regime in Iraq.

In 1978-9, the KDPI joined with other progressive organisations in overthrowing first the Shah and then the Islamic Republic in the Kurdish part of Iran. Violent clashes between Kurds and the new Revolutionary Government broke out almost immediately. Police stations along the border had been captured by Kurdish guerrillas who now controlled most Kurdish towns and large areas of mountainous territory. Khomeini's response was to ban the KDPI and to execute Kurdish rebels. Finally the towns fell to the Revolutionary Guards and the Kurds returned to guerrilla fighting.

Kurds in Iraq

Until the end of the First World War, the Kurds were under either the Shah of Iran or the Ottoman Sultan. However, this authority was not completely accepted by the Kurds. During the First World War, there was an absence of any centralised authority which allowed for widespread disorder. The British occupied the two southern Iraqi provinces from 1914 and extended it over the whole of Mosul province in 1918. Local figures were appointed to administer the area with British political advisors. However, the British government gradually became committed to the establishment of an Arab state under British auspices in Iraq and did not consider an independent Kurdish state. Also, at this time, the Kurds were fragmented because of traditional clan and tribal rivalries.

In Iraq, the League of Nations decided that Mosul should be part of Iraq and in 1926 the Prime Minister of Iraq declared that civil servants in the Kurdish area should be Kurds, that Kurdish and Arabic should be the official languages of the area and the Kurdish children should be educated in Kurdish. However, the Anglo-Iraqi treaty of 1930 did not include any guarantees for minority groups. From 1947 to 1958 in Iraq, the Kurds had certain basic freedoms whilst in Iran and Turkey, Kurds were persecuted.

The early rebellions were not noticeably nationalistic, but once Barzani withdrew to Iran in 1945 and joined forces with the Mahabad Republic, his efforts took on a more nationalistic hue. When the 1958 revolution in Iraq brought a pro-Soviet government to power, Barzani returned to Iraq from exile in the Soviet Union and founded the Iraqi branch of the KDP.

Qasim who came to power in Iraq in 1958, was not willing to grant real autonomy to the Kurds and, in addition, there was a split between Qasim and the leader, Mulla Mustafa. The war which began between the central government and the Kurds in 1961, continued intermittently until 1975. When the Ba'ths overthrew Qasim in 1963, they had previous assurances from the KDP and Barzani that the Kurds would announce a cease-fire in exchange for discussion on Kurdish autonomy. However, this did not materialise and fighting broke out again.

The Ba'th government, which came to power in a coup in 1968, made a peace agreement with Barzani in March 1970 to end a decade of violence in Iraqi Kurdistan. By the end of 1972, the agreement had fallen apart, the Kirkuk oilfields in particular being a serious point of contention. In 1974, Barzani began a major Kurdish rebellion with up to 100,000 peshmergas. The government carried out atrocities to terrorise the inhabitants into submission after raids on the Iraqi Petroleum Company's installations. Large numbers of families were forcibly removed from their homes to change the ethnic balance of particular areas and, in 1971, 40,000 Kurds were expelled to Iran. From February to March 1973, thousands of Kurds were forced to leave their homes. In 1974, fighting broke out in earnest with the Iraqi Air Force bombing Qala Diza, Galala and Halabja. A mass exodus of refugees took place to Iran in 1975. The Algiers agreement between Iran and Iraq in 1975, closed the Iran-Iraq frontier in the north, thus preventing aid reaching the Kurds from Iran and also preventing the Kurds from regrouping and rearming in and from Iran. By 1979, an estimated 200,000 Kurds had been deported from the frontier area and some 700 villages burnt down to clear a strip along the borders with Iran and Turkey.

Kurdistan had become the main focus of opposition to the dictatorship in Baghdad. In 1981, there were strikes and demonstrations throughout the Kurdish area. Hundreds of executions and many thousands of deportations and "relocations" followed. Saddam Husain used chemical weapons to depopulate large strategic areas of Iraqi Kurdistan. Many tens of thousands of civilians were killed and their use was effective in persuading villagers to abandon their homes and farms and flee as refugees. The attack on Halabja in March 1988 killed 5-6000 people. Following the cease-fire with Iran (1988), chemical weapons were used on military and civilian targets as an integral part of the government's 1988 offensive to mop up the Kurdish resistance now bereft of Iranian support. Further attacks using poison gas were also recorded.

During the Gulf War (1990-1991), there was a mass exodus of refugees from Iraqi Kurdistan and "safe havens" in Dohuk province to the north-west, were set up by the British and Americans. However, masses of refugees fleeing the provinces of Kirkuk, Arbil and Sulaimaniyya, remained in the open at Saddam's mercy without aid or protection, trapped between the Iraqi army and the border with Iran. In October 1991, the Iraqi government suddenly withdrew from the main Kurdish areas and imposed a strict embargo, leaving the Kurds as the sole authority in charge. Iran, Turkey and Syria began holding regular meetings to discuss the Kurdish situation and publicly declared they would not tolerate Kurdish independence or the break-up of Iraq.

Further Reading

The Kurds and Kurdistan by *J. Leatherby*, 1989, Refugee Studies Programme
Iraq since the Gulf War edited by *Fran Hazelton,* 1994, Zed Books
Saddam's Iraq by *Cardri,* 1986, Zed Books
Kurdistan Report, Kurdistan Solidarity Committee and Kurdistan Information Centre, May/June 1995
A Modern History of the Kurds by *D. McDowall*, 1997, Taurus

Bosnia

Language

Historically, the Slavic peoples of the region chose their alphabets in the 10th and 11th centuries on an essentially religious basis. The Serbs and Macedonians adopted the Orthodox Cyrillic alphabet. The Slovenes adopted Latin script, as did the Croats. The Bosnians wrote in a similar script termed "bosancica".

The Yugoslav Federation, which grew out of the Kingdom of Serbs, Croats and Slovenes, a product of the First World War, was from its inception dominated by Serbian influences in the law, politics and military. The name "Serbo-Croat" was coined for an essentially Serbian-based official language. The phenomenon of the Serbo-Croat language ignored the quite separate and unique languages of Macedonia and Slovenia, the dialects of Bosnia-Hercegovina and the Croatian language.

The break-up of Yugoslavia has been mirrored linguistically and long-buried books are reappearing so that language and literature are being used to assert identity. In 1992, a new lexicon detailing the differences between Serbian and Croatian was published in Zagreb.

Literature

Although Yugoslavia was communist, the position of literature and the writer in relation to the authorities and censorship in Yugoslavia, was viewed with envy and admiration by the majority of writers in the Eastern bloc countries.

However, after the Second World War, post-revolutionary Yugoslavia followed very much the dictates of Moscow and there was strict Party control of literature. Yugoslav literature has three main traditions — Serb, Croat and Slovene. In the past, these widely differing regional areas of literary activity functioned for long periods almost independently. The two predominant features of earlier periods were traditional regionalism and naive lyricism. However, in modern times, after the Second World War and before the break-up of Yugoslavia, wider and more universal themes, such as the country's traumatic experiences during the War, became more important. There was considerable contact between the different literary centres so that literary trends converged. However, it was still difficult to speak of a "Yugoslav literature".

One of the most famous writers was Ivo Andric who was born in 1892 in Bosnia. Until 1941, he served as a Yugoslav diplomat. When he was placed under house arrest in Belgrade by the occupying Germans, Andric turned to writing. In 1961 he was awarded the Nobel Prize for literature. His best-known novel is *The Bridge Over the Drina,* published in Serbo-Croat. He died in 1975. Ivan V. Lalic is one of former Yugoslavia's most eminent poets, who first rose to prominence during the creative wave that followed the lifting of Communist Party control of literature in the 1950s.

Serb literature — Modern Serbian literature has its crude beginnings in the last two decades of the eighteenth century. The revival of literary life was closely connected with national aspirations against Ottoman rule and the Church imposed a written language, Slavic-Serbian, on the intellectuals. The only literature in the people's language at this time was still folk poetry. Petar Petrovic Njegos wrote epic poetry such as *The Mountain Wreath* which depicted an important moment in the history of the Montenegrin heroic struggle against the Turks. Branko Radicevic was a Serb poet. This Romantic movement in Serbian literature began in the 1840s and was replaced by a new movement "Realism". Practically all the new writers such as Milovan Glisic, Laza Lazarevic and Janko

Veselinovic, reflected in their works their new awareness of existing social concerns although they were closely attached to their home town or narrow region. The first two decades of the twentieth century saw new trends referred to as the Moderna which had been influenced by literary movements in Europe. After the First World War there was a new generation of authors and poets such as Milos Crnjanski and Rastko Petrovic who used more forceful expression in poetry and literature. Other writers followed the traditional realistic line. Ivo Andric was a significant storyteller who wrote *The Bridge Over the Drina, The Chronicle of Travnik* and *Miss.* Mihailo Lalic, who is considered the best living Serbian writer next to Andric, produced his greatest novel *The Wailing Mountain.*

Croatian literature — After World War 2, a trend imitating the Soviet brand of Socialist Realism was introduced. However, after 1950, this literary dogma began to lose its importance and Croatian writers started looking for a new and more realistic approach to literature. Some Croatian writers are Ranko Marinkovic, Vladan Desnica, Vesna Parun and Peter Segedin. Marinkovic's best known novel is *Cyclops* (1965) which analyses the psychological make-up of present day man and his life. Desnica is a poet and short story writer in the tradition of Croatian realism while Vesna Parun is one of the leading and most original post war Croatian poets.

The war has resulted in the dispersion of many writers and poets e.g. Himzo Skorupan who had six novels published in the former Yugoslavia.

Further Reading

New Writing in Yugoslavia by *Bernard Johnson* 1970, Penguin
Introduction to Yugoslav Literature by *B. Mikosinovich et al* Twayne, New York, 1973

Political/Historical Background

Yugoslavia was founded in 1918 after the First World War. The seven regions in the Balkan Peninsula which united to form Yugoslavia were Slovenia, Serbia, Croatia, Dalmatia, Montenegro, Bosnia-Hercegovina and Macedonia, with each having very different histories and religions. Bosnia and Hercegovina were Ottoman possessions for four centuries when the Slavs converted to Islam. This was considered alien to and a conscious rival of both the Orthodox Russian and the civilisation of Western Europe. 41% of Bosnia Hercegovina's population is Muslim. After the Ottomans were overthrown, the area came under the Hapsburg administration from 1878. In 1908, Austria-Hungary sealed its possession of the provinces by formally annexing them to stop the Kingdom of Serbia gaining from the collapse of Ottoman Turkey.

The Nazis invaded Yugoslavia in 1941 and created a puppet state in Croatia with the support of Croatian fascists. This state included parts of Bosnia-Hercegovina and Serbia. During the Second World War in Bosnia, atrocities were inflicted by the Catholic Croatian fascists, the Ustashe, against the Muslims, Serbs, Jews, Roma and anti-fascist Croats. A revolution took place in Yugoslavia during the Second World War. This brought the communists to power under Tito and a new state was founded in 1945. The political system was designed to prevent any of the different groups of peoples feeling a grievance, with all being equal and having the same rights of autonomy. In 1947, Yugoslavia participated in the foundation of an organisation of the Eastern Bloc communist parties which had its headquarters in Belgrade. Subsequently, there was a quarrel between Yugoslavia and the Soviet Union over the issue of national independence.

With the collapse of eastern European communism in 1990, Yugoslavia started to break up. In 1991 Croatia and Slovenia declared their independence. In Croatia, a Serb minority rebelled against the moves towards Croatian independence. Thousands were killed. UN peace-keeping forces were then stationed in Croatia. In February 1992, nationalist pressures caused the Government of Bosnia-Hercegovina to declare independence. Bosnian Serbs then proclaimed their own state and soon after, Serbian forces attacked Sarajevo and other Bosnian cities. During the siege of Sarajevo, Bosnian Serb forces dropped more than five hundred thousand mortar and artillery shells on Sarajevo and ten thousand people died. By the end of 1992, regular soldiers, formerly of the Yugoslav People's Army, and irregular Serb militia had gained control of 70 per cent of Bosnia-Hercegovina. Bosnian Croats seized control of most of western Hercegovina and central Bosnia and also proclaimed their own state. Although the Muslims were the largest ethnic group, they were driven out of large parts of Bosnia-Hercegovina during campaigns of ethnic cleansing. Mass expulsion combined in instances with murder and terror against whole populations was used to "solve" the problem of dividing Bosnia-Hercegovina's territory with its previous intricate ethnic mix. Terrible atrocities took place with the Serbian forces accused of committing the largest numbers of human rights violations. The war lasted four years.

NATO attempted to end the war but it was finally ended by the American bombing of Serb positions. The Dayton Peace Accord, drawn up by the Americans, was signed in December 1995. Basically it said that the Republic of Bosnia and Hercegovina would continue as a sovereign state within its internationally recognised borders. It would be composed of two entities, the Federation of Bosnia and Hercegovina which would control 51% of the territory and the Serb Republic which would hold the remainder. The capital, Sarajevo, would be re-unified within the Muslim-Croat Federation.

There have been many problems around civilian re-settlement and there is still sporadic fighting and victimisation when Muslims try to return to their homes in Serb territory. Although the Dayton peace agreement stipulated that refugees should be allowed to go home, the Bosnian Serbs, who control 49% of Bosnia, have blocked Muslims. Thousands of Muslim men are missing, believed to have been killed. The Serb leader, Dr Karadzic and his commander-in-chief, Ratko Mladic, are on the list of war criminals, indicted by the War Crimes Tribunal in The Hague.

Further Reading

Yugoslavia by *Phyllis Auty,* Thames and Hudson, 1965
War Report, Institute for War and Peace Reporting
Former Yugoslavia, Refugee Council Factsheet 7, 1994
Bosnia, A Short History by *Noel Malcolm,* 1994, Macmillan
A Paper House by *Mark Thompson,* 1992, Hutchinson & Radius

Iraq

Cultural/Literary Background

Classical poetry was of great importance. Major poets were Nabigha al-Dhubiani (535-604), Abu Tammam (788-845), Mutanabbi (915-65) and Ibn Zaidun (1003-70). A reading of Arab poetry from the last hundred years shows two distinct developments. While some poets turned to classical poetry for inspiration, others successfully blended classical Arab tradition with European modernism.

Modern Arabic poetry can be traced from Ameen Rihani (1876-1940) and Gibran Kahlil Gibran (1883-1931), who revived the pre-Islamic and Sufi concept of the poet as a visionary and introduced two new poetic forms — free verse and prose poem. Poetry ceased to be a description of reality as seen through a window and expressed in a received language. Gibran's major contribution to Arab poetry is his revolutionary attitude to the establishment and to language. He brutally attacked the hypocrisy and corruption of the political, religious and social order of the day. He also injected a new force and resonance into language.

The link in Iraq between culture and politics was firmly established in the 1940s and 50s. One of the major trends in modern Arab poetry was the Taf'ila Movement (1947-57) in Iraq. This was a modern, experimental poetry movement led by Al-Mala'ika, Al-Sayyab, Al-Bayati and Buland al-Haidari. The majority of writers in Iraq were sympathetic to the Marxist or nationalist political groups in opposition. Influential daily newspapers were edited by intellectuals such as the great Arab poet, Muhammad Mahdi al-Jawahiri. However, the government used various methods to restrict an independent cultural movement. It interfered with the circulation of books, prohibited cul-

193

tural imports and imposed censorship. Many writers such as the poets, Badr Shakir al-Sayyab, Al-Bayati and Sa'di Yusuf, were arrested or exiled.

The revolutionary government of July 1958 used publishing houses and the media as instruments of state propaganda. In 1963 the Ba'thist coup overthrew the leader, Qasim, and hundred of intellectuals were imprisoned, tortured, executed or forced into exile. The Arab defeat by Israel in 1967, affected Arab culture in that it entered a phase of despair but also change. In Iraq in 1968, there was a radical literary and artistic upsurge in which quasi-religious dogmas were abandoned and the subservience of literature to politics was widely denounced. Many poets were deeply affected by Western literature.

The second Ba'thist regime, which came to power in July 1968, tried to please intellectuals by inviting Iraqi writers in exile to return home and build a new cultural movement. However, it met resistance from intellectuals who vividly remembered the bloodshed of the first Ba'thist regime (Feb-Nov 1963).

The late sixties and early seventies were years of great tension in Iraqi cultural life. In 1977, Saddam Husain embarked on a programme of purging all journals and cultural agencies of non-Ba'thist employees. In 1979, the security and intelligence services were given a free hand to manipulate cultural life as they wished. More than two hundred poets, storytellers, musicians, theatre directors, film-makers and painters were arrested and tortured. Many were executed, died under torture or were poisoned. More than seven hundred Iraqi intellectuals fled the country. A mass culture has been created which serves purely as a means of Ba'th Party control over the Iraqi people.

During the Iran-Iraq War (1980-88), popular poetry, written in colloquial Iraqi dialect, was an important means of mobilising the masses for war. In literature only one theme was officially sanctioned — the actual victory. The function of literature was to glorify martyrdom, making life inferior to death. In 1981, a large number of writers were sent to the Iran-Iraq war zone by the Minister for Culture. Those who objected were subject to harsh penalties.

A new generation of intellectuals has been created to work in culture as a department of the state. These are the "state intellectuals" who devote their energies to supporting the "machine of state" which is merciless towards opposition or dissent. Intellectuals not integrated into the official establishment face continuous intimidation, threats of imprisonment, torture and death. Abd al-Wahhab al Daini, a prominent playwright, was sentenced to life imprisonment on the basis of a secretly tape-recorded conversation in which he criticised the government. His whereabouts are unknown.

Saddam Husain has used brutality and bribery to secure totalitarian control of Iraqi intellectual life. The regime has a cultural code of its own: literature, aesthetics and a notion of history are centred on the role of the absolute leader as a saviour with whom the destiny of the nation is identified. The veneration of the leader requires endless songs of praise, poems and novels by approved writers.

In Iraq, the writer was in direct contact with the readers because, traditionally, he read his works to large groups of people in the streets or cafes and was a known figure in the area. Many writers in exile now write for an Arab readership living mainly in Arabic speaking countries. They are, therefore, unable to continue the same relationship. Writers and poets in exile include Abdul Karim Kassid (London), Zuhair Al Jazairi (London), Sargon Boulos (USA), Fawzi Kerim (London) and Haifa Zangana (London). Buland al-Haidari, who was in exile in London, died in 1996. He is considered to be one of the founders of modern Arab poetry.

Further Reading

Modern Poetry of the Arab World, translated and edited by *Abdullah al-Udhari*, 1986, Penguin
Iraq since the Gulf War, edited by *Fran Hazelton*, 1994, Zed Books, (Cultural Totalitarianism by Fatima Mohsen)
Modern Arab Poets, translated and edited by *Issa J. Boullata*, 1982, Heinemann

Political/historical Background

Before 1914, Iraq was three provinces of the Ottoman Empire. Britain occupied this territory during the First World War and in 1920 was awarded the mandate over Iraq by the League of Nations. King Faisal ruled Iraq from 1921 to 1933 and was responsible for forming the Iraqi Army. Iraq became an independent state in 1932. The years of nominal independence from 1932 were characterised by *coups d'etat*. Post-war, there was a struggle for national liberation and democratic rights with the overthrow of the pro-British Nuri Sa'id regime in 1958 by General Abd al-Karim Qasim. The 1958 Revolution achieved Iraq's national independence and a programme of land reform, but 1958 to 1963 were years of intense struggle between the Communists, Pan-Arab Nationalists and Ba'thists about how radical the revolution should be.

In February 1963, a *coup d'etat* brought the Ba'th Party to power in an orgy of bloodshed. They were overthrown in November 1963 by a military nationalist coup after which a succession of governments ruled until the Ba'th party regained power in July 1968. There were attempts by the Ba'th party in the early 1970s to gain wider support by forming a national alliance with some of the opposition parties. However, they refused any democratisation. From 1978, there was an increasingly terrorist one-party rule which culminated in violent repression of all opposition. Saddam Husain seized the presidency in July 1979 and

196

physically eliminated his opponents and rivals in the Ba'th party.

The overthrow of the Shah of Iran in 1979 had a traumatic effect on all the reactionary rulers in the Middle East. In Iraq, the ruling junta was alarmed by the example of millions of unarmed Iranians overthrowing a regime. The Ba'th government gave refuge to the deposed Shah's generals, to his former prime minister and to the SAVAK secret police. In 1980, when the Iran-Iraq War began, tens of thousands of Shi'ite Iraqis were deported as they were alleged to be of Iranian origin.

The Iraqi army invaded Iran in September 1980. The Iran-Iraq War was launched by Saddam Husain in an attempt to solve his internal crisis, dominate the Gulf, lead the Arab world and contain the Iranian revolution. This war lasted eight years with huge loss of life. Battlefield casualties are thought to be one million. Families were expected to celebrate for having given a "martyr" to the war and the regime rewarded these families with free agricultural land, houses and pensions. The final insult came when the regime began to extend its rewards to anyone marrying a widow. Over ten towns and cities were destroyed and the Iraqi economy was ruined. Commercial ships were sunk in the Gulf in 1983, there were air attacks on cities and towns in 1984 and chemical weapons were used. The human tragedy of the war was linked to the escalation of repression against democratic forces and against any opposition to the war.

In August 1990, Saddam Husain invaded, occupied, annexed and sacked Kuwait. An Allied coalition of thirty nations then defeated Iraq in the Gulf War which ended in March 1991. Iraq's economy, water and health facilities were destroyed by bombing. After the Gulf War all UN member states were ordered to enforce strict sanctions against Iraq. These included an embargo on all trade to Iraq and on exports of oil which made up more than 90% of Iraq's exports before the Gulf War. This embargo will remain until the Iraqi government has destroyed all its chemical weapons and ended its nuclear weapons' research programme. The sanctions are causing great hardship to civilians but, despite the suffering which Saddam Husain has inflicted on his people, he remains in power.

Further Reading

Saddam's Iraq by *Cardri*, 1986, Zed Books
Iraq Since The Gulf War Edited by *Fran Hazelton*, 1994, Zed Books

Angola

Literary/Cultural Background

The official language is Portuguese. Other languages are Kimbundu, Kikongo, Cokwe, Luvale, Lunda, Umbundu, Fioti, Ngangela etc. All Angolan languages are closely related and are Bantu languages.

Angolan poetry by Angolan writers in Portuguese dates from about 1949. Assimilationist attitudes and directives caused the emergence of a detribalised literature. The literature in Portuguese had little relationship with tribal consciousness and the literature in vernacular languages was very limited in output. The modern period in Angolan poetry began with the slogan "Let's discover Angola" and with the cultural movement whose giant figures were Agostino Neto, Antonio Jacinto and Viriato da Cruz, respectively black, white and mestico (mixed blood) Angolans. Other well-known poets were Costa Andrade, Mario Antonio and Arnaldo Santos who depicted daily life in the African quarters of Luanda. The modern movement flourished in Angola, despite colonial interference, until about 1960, when increased repression by the Portuguese colonial political police drove Angolan poets into hiding, prison, exile and guerrilla warfare. From 1961 to 1974, poets were silenced within their own country but continued to write in prison or at the battlefront. Some were exiled to the Cape Verde Islands. Literature, principally poetry, was one of the first weapons in the Angolan people's modern struggle against Portuguese colonial domination. Poets wrote about the historical suffering of the Angolan people through slavery and forced labour and about the continuing burden of imprisonment or exile. When independence was achieved in 1975, they returned to Angola. Arlindo Barbeitos drew on his experiences of combat to write a collection of poems called *Angola, hail Angola, Angola the word*. Pepetela wrote a short novel called *The adventures of Ngunga* which sold over 75,000 copies in Angola alone.

Jose Luandino Vieira emerged as Angola's most prominent writer of fiction and chronicler of Luanda's Creole-Kimbundu hegemony. *Luanda,* Vieira's first major work, was banned by the Portuguese while the author was serving an eleven year prison term for his nationalist activities. Antonio Agostinho Neto, the poet-president of Angola led the way in stressing literature's role in the cultural revolution. Although most of the works published since independence focused on anti-colonialism and cultural revindication, new forms and styles of writing did appear. A more recent writer is Uanhenga Xitu who writes about the people and customs of his Kimbundu homeland although he writes in Portuguese.

Since the early eighties, economic crises, military aggression and the demands of building up a new nation have curtailed the recent development of Angolan literature.

The Angolan writing in the book includes Sousa Jamba who is resident in Britain. He has been a winner of the Spectator's "Shiva Naipaul Prize" and he has written two novels — *Patriots* and *The Loneliest Devil*.

Writings by Antonio Cabral and Antonio Joaquim Marques are also included.

Further Reading

African Literatures in the Twentieth Century by *L.S. Klein*, 1988, Oldcastle Books
Luaanda by *Jose Luandino Vieira*, 1980, Heinemann Educational
Poems from Angola by *Michael Wolfers*, 1979, Heinemann Educational
The World of Mestre Tamoda by *Uanhanga Xitu*, 1988, Readers International

Political/Historical Background

In 1974, the Portuguese withdrew from Angola. They had ruled it for four hundred years but could no longer fight off the rebel forces that were struggling for their independence. These rebel forces were the MPLA, UNITA and the FNLA. When the Portuguese moved out, these groups fought amongst themselves. The Russians saw this as an opportunity to gain influence over a coastal African state from which they could threaten the West's oil routes. They, therefore, sent in Cuban soldiers to help the MPLA who quickly defeated the other factions and set up a government in 1975.

However, by 1980, this government was being challenged. SWAPO guerrillas were attacking from Namibia. Unita reappeared and with the help of South Africa, they even penetrated into the northern parts of Angola. Political allegiences were determined by tribal loyalty with the Ovimbundu supporting Unita and the Kimbundu supporting the Marxist MPLA. In 1991, the two warring sides signed a peace accord after sixteen years of civil war. The first democratic elections were held in 1992 when Jonas Savimbi, the Unita leader, was defeated. He attributed his defeat by Jose Eduardo dos Santos, the president and MPLA leader, to electoral fraud and withdrew to Huambo in the heart of the Ovimbundu territory. Unita was flushed out of the capital, Luanda, and during the confrontation, the government armed groups of vigilantes who backed the police in its assault on all Unita offices. Having destroyed all the Unita offices, clinics and hostels and shot dead several of its high-ranking leaders, the vigilantes began a door-to-door search for members of the Ovimbundu tribe.

Unita reorganised its army and began to seize towns and villages. Between 1993 and 1994, the civil war escalated with both sides laying land mines. Attempts to negotiate a ceasefire failed. Both Unita and the MPLA have killed, imprisoned or executed people suspected of supporting opposition groups. Under the terms of the Lusaka Peace Protocol, signed in 1994 by the government and Unita, the Angolan army started to withdraw to barracks in 1996 and there was an uneasy peace. A new government of national unity was installed in 1997, to formalise the end of twenty years of bloody conflict.

The civil war has devastated countless lives, torn communities and families apart and led to human rights abuses on a massive scale. The landmines have caused an enormous amount of people to lose limbs. Many Angolans have fled to Portugal, Zaire, Namibia and Zambia.

Further Reading

BBC *Focus on Africa* magazines
African Ethnic Cleansing by *Sousa Jamba*, 21.11.92, The Spectator
Superpower Relations since 1945 by *Larry Hartley*, 1989, Unwin Hyman
Angola — The Lusaka Protocol, 1996, Amnesty International

The Contributors

Maxamed Daahir AFRAX is a refugee from Somalia who currently resides in London. Afrax's works include novels, short stories, plays and literary criticism in Somali and Arabic.

Ibrahim AHMED is from Iraq and currently lives in Sweden.

Ahmed Omar ASKAR is a Somali writer currently living in Finland.

Reza BARAHENI is an Iranian writer. He is the author of three novels and two dozen short stories, most of which have not been published in Iran as they were suppressed by the censor. He spent three months in prison in Teheran. He was in solitary confinement for 102 days. After his release, he left Iran for the United States.

Cikuru BATUMIKE was born in Zaire and now lives in exile in Switzerland after having been imprisoned in Zaire. He was a journalist and has published various collections of poetry.

Sherko BEKAS is a Kurdish poet who is currently in exile in Sweden.

Sargon BOULOS is an Iraqi poet and short story writer, who emigrated to the United States.

Antonio CABRAL is from Angola and came to the UK for a graduate course but was unable to return. He needs to write to connect himself with his culture. He writes in Umbundu.

Ahmad EBRAHIMI is chair of the Iranian PEN Centre in Exile and lives in London. He came to Britain in 1974 for post-graduate studies and subsequently worked as an economist. He published his first volume of poetry in 1974 and also writes short stories.

Zlata FILIPOVIC was born in Sarajevo in 1980 and began writing a diary *Zlata's Diary* during the siege of Sarajevo. She is now in exile in Paris with her parents.

Diangitukwa FWELEY is from Zaire and currently lives in exile in Switzerland. He was a professor of French in Kinshasa and also a journalist in the Department of Culture and Arts. He has published a collection of poetry, a play and a narrative.

Munzur GEM is a Kurdish writer from Turkey who is currently in exile in Sweden.

'HADRAAWI' is a revered Somali poet who lives in exile in Britain. In 1973 he was imprisoned for composing poems interpreted as being critical of the Government. Later he joined the Somali National Movement and was a key member of the Ethiopean-based opposition.

Buland AL-HAIDARI was a famous Iraqi poet who lived in exile first in Lebanon and then in London. He died in London in 1996. A considerable number of his collections of poetry have been published including *Songs of the Tired Guard* and *Dialogue in Three Dimensions*.

Sousa JAMBA was born in Angola, fled at the time of the civil war to Zambia and later returned to join UNITA against the MPLA government. He now lives in London. He was a regular contributor to *The Spectator* and has had two novels published.

Miroslav JANCIC is from former Yugoslavia and is currently in exile in Britain where he writes in English rather than in his own language. He was born in Sarajevo and is a Bosnian writer with three novels, ten plays/film scripts and two books of non-fiction to his credit. When the war started in 1992, he was the ambassador to Ghana.

Zuhair AL-JAZAIRI is from Iraq where he was a journalist. He currently lives in exile in London. He has had eleven books published including a novel and short stories.

Abdul Karim KASSID is an Iraqi poet with five published books of peotry to his name. He now lives in exile in London and edits the Arabic literary magazine *NSUS*. He has lived in Lebanon, France and Algeria where he worked as a University lecturer.

Fawzi KERIM is from Iraq and currently lives in exile in London. He has had eight books of poetry published as well as fiction.

Mohammed Khaki is a Kurdish poet from Iran currently living in exile in London. He has written four volumes of poetry.

Esmail KHO'I is from Iran and is currently in exile in Britain. He has published twelve collections of poetry and some of his poems have been translated into several languages. He has written articles of literary and social criticism.

Hadi KHORSANDI is an Iranian satirist in exile in London. Khorsandi was one of Iran's most successful journalists. He is the Editor of the magazine *Asghar Agha* published in London. An unsuccessful plot to assassinate Khorsandi in London, has meant that he must keep a low profile in exile.

Igor Klikovac is a Bosnian poet from Sarajevo who is now in exile in London. His first collection of poetry *The Last Days of Peking*, is now being translated into English, Czech and Slovene. He is editor of *Stone Soup*, a bilingual English and ex-Yugoslav literary magazine.

Antonio Joaquim Marques (Kiluanji Kush) has published several collections of poetry. *Journey of Search*, 1989. *Mystic Verses* and *Scarlet Voices*, 1990. In 1991 he originated a poetry form called ETU with the publication of a volume entitled *Sun Woman*. In 1993 he published *Flames of New Dreams*.

He is currently working on a long poem entitled *The Last Turning Point* which will complete his trilogy, *Turbulent Passages*. Antonio Joaquim Marques is Angolan, resident in Scandinavia. He speaks seven languages.

Dieudonne Marcelle Makenga is from Zaire.

Semezdin Mehmedinovic was until recently living in Sarajevo. He now lives in exile. He is a poet and short story writer.

Hushang Mehr-Ayin fled from Iran in 1982 and currently lives in exile in Britain. He is the author of a banned novel *Eclipse in Pentagon City* and other short stories, also banned.

Kamal Mirawdeli is Kurdish from Iraq and currently lives in exile in London. He has written on a wide range of subjects covering literature, history, politics and philosophy and has published two volumes of poems.

Abdirahman Mirreh is from Hargeisa, Somalia. He obtained degrees in Tropical Agriculture and Anthropology and then studied and worked in Norway before returning to Somalia in 1982 where he was when war broke out. He now lives in exile in Norway.

Fouad MIRZA is from Iraq. He currently lives in the USA.

Mabiala MOLU is from Zaire and currently lives in France.

Muepu MUAMBA is from Zaire and is currently in enforced exile in France and Germany.

Pius Ngandu NKASHAMA is from Zaire and now lives in exile in France. He was a founder of literary drama in Zaire and is a poet, essayist, novelist and playwright. He has had a large number of works published. He taught at the universities of Annaba, Algeria and Leiden and is currently a professor at the University of Limoges, France. He writes in French.

Ghazi RABIHAVI is an Iranian writer whose stories are banned in his own country.

Rafiq SABIR is a Kurdish poet in exile in Sweden. He joined the Kurdish movement in 1978 and his life as a 'peshmerga' became the source of his many poems.

Sadiq AL-SAYGH is an Iraqi poet.

Mojdeh SHAHRIARI is an Iranian writer who lives in exile in Canada.

Dara SEKULIC has been a well-known poet in Bosnia for forty years. She is now in exile in Germany.

Ahmad SHAMLOO is one of Iran's most respected poets. In the past, he was arrested and forced into hiding or into exile.

Sasa SKENDERIJA is a Bosnian poet now living in exile in Prague. The poem in this section is from his second book of poetry called *It's Never Like It Is In The Movies*.

Himzo Skorupan came to Britain from the former Yugoslavia in 1992. He worked as a journalist and had six novels published in Serbo-Croat. He has written two unpublished books whilst living in Britain. He is a Bosnian refugee.

Dubravka Ugresic is from Croatia and is the author of three children's books and two collections of short stories. She currently lives in exile in Berlin.

Amina Ahmed Yusuf is a Somali poet who is currently in exile in London.

Haifa Zangana was born in Iraq and studied pharmacy. She left Iraq to work in Syria and in 1976 left Syria for London where she works as a journalist. Her novel *Through the Vast Halls of Memory* was published in 1991.

* * *

Jennifer Langer, herself the daughter of refugee parents, lives in London. She works in the field of adult and further education for bilingual students, has co-ordinated refugee education projects in different London colleges and is also a trainer and moderator. Jennifer Langer is the author of the *ESOL Refugee Pack* and *The System in Britain*. She works closely with refugees from Africa, the Middle East and Bosnia and is actively involved in working for Middle East peace.

Ron Waddams, the cover artist, is a Quaker whose art is a spiritual journey which reflects his lifelong concern for peace, particularly through support for the United Nations Association.

Teaching Pack

A Teaching Pack for use with *The Bend in the Road* is
available for £2 from:

Five Leaves Publications,
PO Box 81,
Nottingham NG5 4ER.